# Underexploited Tropical Plants with Promising Economic Value

Report of an Ad Hoc Panel of the Advisory
   Committee on Technology Innovation
Board on Science and Technology for
   International Development
Commission on International Relations

Avec résumé en français
Con resumen en español

NATIONAL ACADEMY OF SCIENCES
Washington, D.C.   1975

This report has been prepared by an ad hoc advisory panel of the Board on Science and Technology for International Development, Commission on International Relations, National Research Council, for the Office of Science and Technology, Bureau for Technical Assistance, Agency for International Development, Washington, D.C., under Contract No. csd-2584.

Illustrations by Elmer W. Smith, Cambridge, Massachusetts.

iii

ROY WHISTLER, Department of Biochemistry, Purdue University, Lafayette, Indiana

NOEL D. VIETMEYER, Board on Science and Technology for International Development, Commission on International Relations, National Academy of Sciences-National Research Council, *Staff Study Director*

\*　　\*　　\*

JULIEN ENGEL, Board on Science and Technology for International Development, Commission on International Relations, National Academy of Sciences, National Research Council, *Head, Special Studies*

# PREFACE

This is a report on plants that show promise for improving the quality of life in tropical areas. Because the countries in this zone contain most of the world's low-income populations this report is addressed to those government administrators, technical assistance personnel, and researchers in agriculture, nutrition, and related disciplines who are concerned with helping developing countries achieve a more efficient and balanced exploitation of their biological resources.

The ad hoc panel on underexploited tropical plants, which produced the report, met at Airlie, Virginia, in March 1974. The panel had the following objectives:

- To identify neglected but seemingly useful tropical plants, both wild and domesticated, that have economic potential;
- To select the plants that showed the most promise for wider exploitation throughout the tropics; and
- To indicate requirements and avenues for research to ensure that selected plants reach their fullest potential.

The 36 plants described here were selected from among 400 nominated by plant scientists around the world in response to a written inquiry. (To keep the project to manageable size, medicinal plants and timber species were excluded.) The choice reflected here is necessarily subjective, based as it is on the experience and judgment of the panel. Plants chosen for inclusion had to satisfy several criteria, the most important of which were:

- Can it be grown in the tropics?
- Does it have significant potential as a source of food, forage, or industrial raw material?
- Can it help make developing countries (or areas within them) more productive?

Other considerations were: Can the plant make a specific contribution to human nutrition? Does the plant have multiple properties enabling several useful products to be obtained from it? The plants were not judged solely by how much or how little is known about them, however. Some of the plants selected are relatively well known; others are taxonomically not yet fully described. Some are "luxury crops" that will appeal only to high-priced specialty markets; others are subsistence crops.

Since it is impossible to determine future costs and benefits of exploiting these plants in vastly dissimilar economic environments, selection could not be based on economic considerations except in the most informal and subjective manner. The task of weighing the technical details against the economics, needs, resources, and capabilities of a particular country or area is perforce left to interested, competent authorities.

The panel recognizes that some plants recommended but finally not selected for inclusion in this report may well have similar potential for exploitation. In such cases, the panel did not have, and could not obtain, enough information to support an affirmative decision.

*The plants presented here should be seen as complements to, not as substitutes for, conventional tropical crops.*

The report aims to provide a brief introduction to the plants selected. It is neither a textbook nor a comprehensive survey of tropical botany. For the convenience of the reader, each plant is presented in a separate chapter, arranged in the following order:

- Description of the plant and of its advantages
- Limitations and special requirements
- Research needs
- Selected readings (significant reviews, general articles)
- Research contacts and germ plasm sources (individuals or organizations known by the panelists to be involved in relevant research or to have appropriate seeds, cuttings, or rootstock).

This report does not detail how to introduce the plants to new areas. Readers should appreciate that achieving this goal may be complex and difficult. Many plants discussed in this report have defied dissemination (or domestication) for a century or more. Plant introduction cannot be divorced from plant management; a lack of horticultural knowledge or experience will frequently cause a plant introduction to fail. Differences in elevation, soil type, temperature, day length, and rainfall present other complications. Sometimes newly introduced plants prove to be too aggressive and become weeds. Even if all these problems are overcome, the plant will be successful only if a market exists or can be created for its products.

The information in this book is only a starting point for what may prove to be laborious and troublesome projects. Addresses of knowledgeable contacts are provided so that readers may ascertain for themselves specific details that cannot be covered in a general report of this kind, but that may be critical to the successful introduction of a plant to their locality.

The panel felt that certain points on the status of tropical botany and the urgency of preserving germ plasm were so important that, although not part of the panel's formal mandate, they are discussed in Chapter 1.

The panel is indebted to the contributors (listed on page 169) and to Mary Jane Koob, who acted as administrative secretary for the meeting and for production of the report. The manuscript was edited and prepared for publication by F. R. Ruskin.

Comments on this report, especially if it has induced initiatives or further research on the species described, should be communicated to the staff officer, Dr. Noel Vietmeyer, National Academy of Sciences-National Research Council, 2101 Constitution Avenue, JH215, Washington, D.C. 20418, USA. Suggestions and information from readers about species not covered in this volume are welcome. They might be included in a later publication.

# CONTENTS

# INTRODUCTION AND SUMMARY

The strain on world resources posed by rapid population growth, dwindling supplies of nonrenewable resources, and shortages of food puts economic botany in the mainstream of human concern.

Throughout history man has used some 3,000 plant species for food; at least 150 of them have been commercially cultivated to some extent. But over the centuries the tendency has been to concentrate on fewer and fewer. Today, most of the people in the world are fed by about 20 crops—cereals such as wheat, rice, maize, millet, and sorghum; root crops such as potato, sweet potato, and cassava; legumes such as peas, beans, peanuts (groundnuts), and soybeans; and sugar cane, sugar beet, coconuts, and bananas. These plants are the main bulwark between mankind and starvation. It is a very small bastion.

Yet as the prospect of food shortages becomes more acute, people must depend increasingly on plants rather than animals for the protein in their diet. As is well recognized, research is urgently needed to increase the yield of these food plants. However, reliance on a small number of plants carries great risk, for monocultures are extremely vulnerable to catastrophic failure brought about by disease or variations in climate. To help feed, clothe, and house a rapidly increasing world population, it is timely to consider neglected or little-known plant species.

Man has only just begun to take stock of the chemical and genetic possibilities in the plant kingdom. Now we must scrutinize the thousands of plant species, many of which are still untested and some as yet unidentified.

The apparent advantages of staple plants over minor tropical plants often result only from the disproportionate research attention they have been given. Many indigenous species may possess equal merit, but were disregarded during the colonial era when consumer demands in European countries largely determined the cultivation (and research) priorities in tropical agriculture. The crops selected (such as banana, pineapple, *Hevea* [rubber], African oil palm, coconuts, and groundnuts) received considerable research and extension. Even after independence, the pattern of concentrating on a few crops changed little. Markets abroad were established, and the new countries needed foreign exchange. Furthermore, as indigenous scientists were generally trained in the institutions of temperate-zone countries they had little interest in studying tropical species. Even the food preference of local populations in tropical colonial countries became so influenced by European food habits that in many places local demand for traditional crops declined.

1

Because of these factors, the potential of many tropical crops has never been explored. A striking case is quinua,* one of the most productive sources of plant protein. It grows high in the Andes, where few other crops can survive. The Spanish introduced wheat and barley and focused agricultural research only on those crops, which eventually displaced quinua. Despite its intrinsic nutritive and economic value and the fact that protein deficiency is a serious problem in its native region, the agronomy of quinua has advanced little in the past four centuries.

## TROPICAL PLANT RESOURCES

Most agricultural scientists are unaware of the scope and potential offered by tropical botany. The discipline suffers largely because the major centers of scientific research are located in temperate zones.

There is an urgent need for plant researchers to become acquainted with tropical plant life. Important new products—such as oils, gums, and waxes for industry; proteins for food and feed; and chemicals for pest control—are likely to result from their attention.

The variety of tropical plant species is staggering. Contained among them is a wealth of new products. In studying tropical economic botany it is not enough to consider solely traditional needs and markets. New raw materials also will be required in the future. Changing conditions are already creating demands for new products from previously underexploited plants; more will be needed as pressures increase for the exploitation of renewable resources.

• Innovations in transportation already make it feasible to transport perishable products around the world.

• Affluence in certain parts of the world has enhanced the consumer's ability to pay for specialty items and heightened his desire for new products such as rare spices, fruit, and fragrances.

• Paradoxically, burgeoning population and continued poverty elsewhere are increasing the need for survival plants and for those hardy species that can be grown in unusable, marginal land.

• Improved scientific knowledge of adverse effects of certain products has created demands for new products, including unsaturated fats, low-calorie sweeteners, and biodegradable pesticides.

• New industrial processes have stimulated the need for larger supplies of materials such as elastomers, lubricating oils, drug-precursors, and waxes.

Tropical plants appear able to meet many of these demands. Given concentrated research, many underexploited plants could follow the develop-

*See page 20.

mental course of the soybean. During the past 50 years the rising need for protein has turned the soybean into a staple in many parts of the world, including the United States, where the plant was once an oddity.

## PRESERVATION OF PLANT GERM PLASM

A massive effort is needed to ensure the survival of endangered plant species throughout the world. It comes as a surprise to most non-botanists to learn that one out of every 10 plants is either extinct or in imminent danger of extinction. Over 20,000 species are now in need of protection. Wanton destruction of natural vegetation is killing many, but the relentless spread of conventional agriculture displaces and destroys many others. Careful preservation and thorough cataloguing are particularly important for little-known plants such as those described in this report. Only in this way will the genetic diversity and healthy stock needed for developing new food crops be assured. Potential breeding stocks, clones, and cultivars will otherwise become extinct.

To this end, the number of botanic gardens, field stations, and habitat reserves containing natural vegetation types must be increased. At present, the number is actually decreasing: rising costs and urban sprawl are making it more difficult for local botanic gardens in tropical countries to survive. And with their demise even existing collections of tropical germ plasm are being lost. To save these service centers and botanic gardens in the tropics, financial support is urgently required. Local governments must be made more aware of the importance of their native flora resources to their country's economic development and of the need to inventory, maintain, and capitalize on their indigenous vegetative materials. The Stockholm Conference on the Human Environment of 1973 recognized this imperative in its proposal for the establishment of an international network of genetic resource stations. The concept is strongly endorsed by the panel.

The number of personnel trained in tropical plant science must also be increased. Today, few institutions in the world offer training in tropical botany, tropical horticulture, and tropical agronomy. Facilities for training and research should be established rapidly because the time left for the study of undisturbed tropical vegetation is limited.

## PLANT INTRODUCTION

Agriculture in the tropical world suffers for lack of mechanisms for systematically and routinely introducing and investigating little-known but potentially useful tropical plants. Because most tropical countries are poor, their experiment stations cannot afford to devote time and money to lesser-known plants. To alleviate this problem, development agencies and foundations concerned with agriculture should consider sponsoring a system of horticultural facilities (in tropical and subtropical developing countries) to pursue agronomic research and extension on lesser-known indigenous and newly introduced species. In part, such facilities could be extensions of the network of international agricultural research institutions already in existence.

A summary of the plants selected by the panel for their high promise follows.

## Cereals and Pseudocereals

*Echinochloa turnerana*. This wild Australian grass, which has never been studied, yields nutritious grain with just one deep watering. It has important potential for dry land farming in arid regions with sporadic rainfall.

Grain Amaranths (*Amaranthus* species). The seeds of these almost totally neglected Central American grain crops have extremely high levels of protein and of the nutritionally essential amino acid, lysine, which is usually deficient in plant protein.

Quinua (*Chenopodium quinoa*). Although the seed of this tall herb is one of the best sources of protein in the vegetable kingdom, quinua is not cultivated outside its high-altitude Andean home.

*Zostera marina*. Exploratory research on this plant might uncover important benefits, for it is a grain-producing, grass-like plant that grows in seawater. Using the sea to grow grain is a novel and highly speculative concept, but Indians on Mexico's west coast have traditionally harvested *Zostera marina* grain for food and flour.

## Roots and Tubers*

Arracacha (*Arracacia xanthorrhiza*). Known as Peruvian parsnip because of the taste and texture of its root, this plant, which looks like celery, is little known outside the highlands of the Andes. In this region its root is often grown instead of potato and costs only half as much to produce. Arracacha has unrealized potential in tropical highlands worldwide.

*Yams (*Dioscorea* spp.). Although yams are too well known for inclusion in this report they are the most nutritious and popular of the conventional, tropical root crops. Nevertheless, they are not so widely cultivated as some of their competitors because they are more costly to produce; research to reduce production costs would be extremely valuable. Research on storage problems is also urgently needed: often 60 percent of the yams harvested are lost to rot.

Cocoyams (*Xanthosoma* spp.). These highly productive root crops are more nutritious than cassava and quite easily produced. Although they are widely distributed, they never have been subjected to a comprehensive improvement program and they appear to have much unrealized potential.

Taro and Dasheens (*Colocasia esculenta*). Intensively cultivated in only a few countries, the high-yielding taro has worldwide tropical potential. Some types grow upland, others grow in waterlogged, swampy soils that otherwise are unproductive. Dasheens are Asian varieties that produce many small, crisp corms that store well.

## Vegetables

Chaya (*Cnidoscolus aconitifolius* and *Cnidoscolus chayamansa*). The leaves of these fast-growing, prolific shrubs are a nutritious, spinach-like, green vegetable. Known only in Central America, chaya deserves testing elsewhere in the tropics.

Hearts of Palm (harvested from *Euterpe, Bactris, Acrocomis, Cocos* palms, etc.). The demand for this delicacy has increased so rapidly during the past 10 years that current supplies are inadequate. Wild stands are being harvested relentlessly. Since extracting the heart kills the palm, plantation cultivation (which appears highly promising economically) must be encouraged before wild stands are destroyed.

Wax Gourd (*Benicasa hispida*). This large, melon-like vegetable is easy to grow and can yield three crops per year. Its outstanding feature is that the fruit can be kept without refrigeration for as long as 12 months.

Winged Bean (*Psophocarpus tetragonolobus*). This climbing bean, important in Southeast Asia and Papua New Guinea but unknown elsewhere, is possibly the tropical counterpart of the soybean. With research, it could perhaps become one of the best sources of usable protein in the tropics.

## Fruits

Durian (*Durio* spp.). The common durian is a large, spiny fruit that is esteemed by many for its taste and reviled by others for its odor. Newly discovered odorless species might be more esthetically acceptable and could open a world market for this crop.

Mangosteen (*Garcinia mangostana*). Perhaps the world's best-tasting fruit, the mangosteen is little known outside its Southeast Asian habitat. Concentrated agronomic and horticultural research would help extend its range to other parts of the very humid tropics—a climate zone that is unsuited to most crops.

Naranjilla (*Solanum quitoense*). Related to, but wholly unlike, tomatoes, this dessert fruit is highly esteemed in Peru, Colombia, Ecuador, and Guatemala, but virtually unknown elsewhere. Its delicious, refreshing juice might become popular in the African and Asian tropics, where the plant could easily flourish.

Pejibaye (*Guilielma gasipaes*). The chestnut-like fruit of this palm is probably the most nutritionally balanced of tropical foods. It contains carbohydrates, protein, oil, minerals, and vitamins. Suited to the wet tropics, the trees, once established, require little care and yield well.

Pummelo (*Citrus grandis*). This large fruit, probably a parent of the grapefruit, is highly prized throughout Southeast Asia. Superior cultivars would become important crops if produced elsewhere in the lowland tropics. Though widely tested in the citrus regions of the world, the cultivars tested never approached the quality of the best from southern Thailand.

Soursop (*Annona muricata*). Well known in the South and Central American tropics, the rich, aromatic flavor of soursop pulp could be more widely enjoyed. The fruit pulp and juice keep well and are potentially profitable exports to Europe and North America.

Uvilla (*Pourouma cecropiaefolia*). This grape-like fruit is almost unheard of outside its homeland in the western part of the Amazon basin. Its agreeable pulp is eaten raw and is also made into wine. It merits trial in other forested lowland regions of the tropics. Absolutely nothing is known about its cultivation or agronomic potential.

## Oilseeds

Babassú (*Orbignya speciosa*). This palm grows in abundance in the Amazon basin and parts of Central America. Though the seeds are rich in oil (very similar to coconut oil in composition), the babassú palm has not been domesticated. The main barriers to its exploitation are the labor required for seed collection and the fact that the extremely hard seeds are difficult to open.

Buffalo Gourd (*Curcurbita foetidissima*). This wild, North American desert gourd, which furnished edible seeds for the American Indians, is a potentially profitable source of edible oil and protein in extremely arid lands. It deserves wider recognition and test planting in all arid regions of the world.

*Caryocar* species. Although Sir Henry Wickham, the initiator of the Malayan rubber industry, promoted this oil source as enthusiastically as he did the rubber tree, *Caryocar* species remain little-known trees growing wild in the Amazon region. They bear large quantities of oily seeds resembling Brazil nuts.

*Jessenia polycarpa.* Native to the Amazon region, this palm bears extraordinarily large bunches of fruit with an oil similar to olive oil in appearance, composition, and quality. It is sold as an edible oil in Bogotá, Colombia, but is virtually unknown to the rest of the world.

Jojoba (*Simmondsia chinensis*). This subtropical, North American desert plant is unique in the vegetable kingdom; it secretes liquid wax in its seeds instead of the glyceride oils secreted by other plants. Liquid waxes are important in industry. They are difficult to synthesize, and the only other source is the sperm whale. The development of jojoba as a crop promises to provide important economic benefits to arid tropical and subtropical regions.

## Forage Crops

*Acacia Albida.* Occurring in savannas of East and West Africa, this leguminous tree is unusual in that it is verdant with foliage and fruit during the dry season. Its leaves and pods, relished by all kinds of livestock, are often the only fodder available at that time.

*Brosimum alicastrum.* This tall, drought-resistant tree bears nutritious leaves and small fruit with starchy seeds. The foliage is enjoyed by livestock. Little known outside Central America, it deserves testing in tropical areas—especially those having prolonged dry seasons—where a forage source is needed.

*Cassia sturtii.* Considered unimportant as forage in its native Australia, this bush is providing nutritious forage year-round in experimental projects in Israel. Its potential needs to be determined in other arid regions of temperate or subtropical climate.

Saltbushes (*Atriplex* spp.). Several Australian species of these shrubs show great promise for arid regions. They produce an abundance of palatable forage, especially in saline soils.

Tamarugo (*Prosopis tamarugo*). A hardy, leguminous tree, native to the forbidding Atacama Desert in Chile, tamarugo grows through a layer of salt sometimes 1 m thick. The nutritional quality of its pods and leaves allows sheep to be stocked at rates approaching those of the best forage areas in the world.

## Other Uses

Burití Palm (*Mauritia flexuosa*). Perhaps the most plentiful palm in the world, the burití is not commercially used. Yet many products—starch, fruit, fiber, and wood—could be obtained from it on a large scale. In the Amazon basin, its native home, it is a plentiful resource that would well repay research and development. There are comparable palms elsewhere in the tropics that should be similarly investigated.

*Calathea lutea*. This tall herb grows wild in swamps in the Amazon basin, but does equally well in plantations in wet regions. Its leaves are coated with a hard-melting wax. Simple to plant and harvest, *Calathea lutea* could provide jobs and income in otherwise unusable tropical swamps.

Candelilla (*Euphorbia antisyphilitica*). This herb from the deserts of northern Mexico has leaves coated with valuable wax. A subsidized Mexican industry has produced and exported it to the United States for several years. Research into the processing and cultivation of candelilla could convert it into a highly profitable crop for arid lands throughout the subtropics.

Guar (*Cyamopsis tetragonoloba*). The high-protein seeds of this Asian plant, which resembles the soybean, contain a gum that is in increasing demand by industry. Because of its unusual properties, the gum has many uses, from making water slide more readily through fire hoses to thickening ice cream. Of all sources for vegetable gums, guar is the most promising.

Guayule (*Parthenium argentatum*). A shrub of Mexican deserts, guayule contains good quantities of latex that closely resembles that from the *Hevea* rubber tree. Technical problems associated with separating the latex from resins and other vegetable matter have prevented its development. But it still holds great promise and, given research, it could become an important source of rubber for production in arid lands.

*Paspalum vaginatum*. This highly salt-tolerant grass withstands inundation by seawater and is recommended for the revegetation of salt-affected regions. It is especially good for stabilizing sandy beaches. Already cultivated successfully in Australia, it provides forage in otherwise unusable coastal marshes.

Ramie (*Boehmeria nivea*). The fiber from this tall, perennial shrub, native to East Asia, has superior qualities—strength and freedom from stretch and shrinkage among others. But its use is restricted by the sticky gum that clings tenaciously to the fiber. Solving the problem of degumming (without weakening the fiber) would give ramie a significant role in tropical agriculture.

Spirulina (*Spirulina platensis* and *Spirulina maxima*). These high-protein algae grow in brackish and alkaline waters. Unlike some other algae, spirulina's large aggregations make it easy to harvest by net or other simple means. It is palatable and is already eaten in Chad and Mexico.

# I CEREALS

## ECHINOCHLOA TURNERANA

*Echinochloa turnerana,** a little-known wild Australian plant, has never been used directly by man, nor has the possibility of cultivating it been investigated. Nevertheless, it offers great promise as a forage and grain crop for arid regions. Its most significant feature is that only a single watering is required for the plant to develop from germination to harvest.

Locally called channel millet, channel sorghum, and native sorghum, it grows almost exclusively in the channel country of inland Australia (see map, p. 11) where it is recognized as one of the most palatable, nutritious, and productive fodder grasses. The grain is eaten by horses, cattle, and sheep and is much sought after by native birds. In addition the leaves, culms, and seed-heads are readily eaten by livestock. Furthermore, the whole plant makes excellent hay.

Field experience indicates that the seed of *Echinochloa turnerana* will not germinate after light rains; deep flooding is required. Deep floods not only induce germination, but allow the plant to complete its development without further water. So, unlike other cereals, it does not require a series of waterings throughout its lifetime.

*Echinochloa turnerana* always grows in fertile, silty clay that cracks deeply when dry and is sporadically subjected to deep flooding. Sites may remain dry for years between floodings. The plant often grows abundantly during spring, summer, or early autumn when floods occur.

*Echinochloa inundata*, similar in appearance and growth habits to *Echinochloa turnerana*, has only recently been identified as a distinct species. It grows in less arid areas than *Echinochloa turnerana*: in swamps and clay soil depressions (that hold water for several weeks after heavy rain), and along streams and ponds. Collectors' notes indicate that it, too, is palatable to livestock, but its nutritional value is unknown.

**Echinochloa turnerana* (Domin) J.M. Black. Family: Gramineae.

9

*Echinochloa turnerana.* (R. G. Silcock)

## LIMITATIONS AND SPECIAL REQUIREMENTS

Almost nothing is known about the agronomy or use of *Echinochloa turnerana*. No attempts have yet been made to domesticate it, and there is little documented information on its botany, germination, growth, environmental requirements, yield, etc.

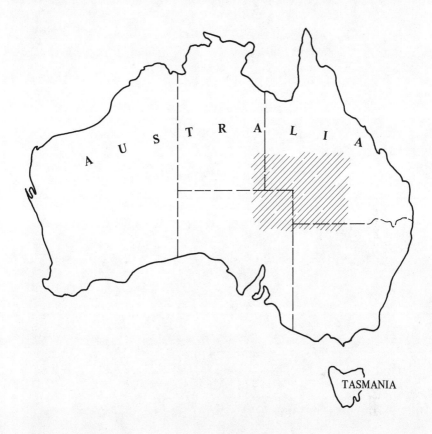

*Echinochloa turnerana*. Known as channel millet, this wild cereal grows in Central Australia's channel country, shown here. This arid region receives an average of 100mm of rain annually, which falls irregularly in only one or two downpours.

Some species of *Echinochloa* are ruinous rice field weeds. The *Echinochloa crus-galli* complex contains some of the weeds most feared by rice growers. The weediness of *Echinochloa turnerana* is unknown, but strict quarantine measures must be enforced during experiments in case it is like its relatives.

In river beds and low-lying regions, *Echinochloa turnerana* grows prodigiously after the soil has been thoroughly soaked. It needs only a single watering to complete its life cycle—an important benefit in arid areas where rainfall is irregular. (S. L. Everist)

Although it is a wild plant never subjected to agronomic improvement, *Echinochloa turnerana* bears dense and heavy seed heads. (S. L. Everist)

## RESEARCH NEEDS

A large collection of seeds is needed for study and distribution and for testing in suitable tropical and subtropical arid and semi-arid lands.

The requirements for germination, growth, and optimum production must be determined.

The genetic behavior (particularly genetic variability and possibilities for selection and breeding of superior strains from wild populations) must be investigated.

Testing with available seed- and forage-harvesting equipment and grain-cleaning equipment should be conducted in Australia.

### Selected Readings

Black, J. M. 1943. *Flora of South Australia. Part 1*, 2nd Ed. Government Printer, Adelaide, Australia. p. 72.
Blake, S. T. 1938. *Proceedings of the Royal Society of Queensland*. 49:187.
Skerman, P. J. 1947. Bureau of investigation technical bulletin number 1. In *The Channel Country of South-west Queensland*. pp. 71-92. Queensland Department of Public Lands, Brisbane, Australia.

### Research Contacts and Germ Plasm Supply

Department of Agronomy, University of Sydney, Sydney, New South Wales 2006, Australia (P. A. Michael)
Director of Agriculture, Department of Primary Industries, William Street, Brisbane, Queensland 4000, Australia
Queensland Herbarium, Meiers Road, Indooroopilly, Queensland 4068, Australia (S. L. Everist, Director)

# GRAIN AMARANTHS

Three promising species of *Amaranthus** are largely neglected candidates for increasing protein production in developing countries. Amaranths are fast-growing, cereal-like plants that produce high-protein grains in large,

*1. *Amaranthus caudatus* L. (*Amaranthus edulis* Speg. is considered a race of this species), 2. *Amaranthus cruentus* L., and 3. *Amaranthus hypochondriacus* L. (also known as *Amaranthus leucocarpus*). Family: Amaranthaceae.

*Amaranthus hypochondriacus.* (Rodale Press, Inc.)

sorghum-like seed heads. Their protein-rich leaves are already widely consumed (a tropical spinach that can be harvested many times a year).

Analyses and feeding experiments demonstrate that *Amaranthus edulis* grain is rich in protein and exceptionally high in lysine—one of the critical amino acids usually deficient in plant protein. In *Amaranthus edulis* 6.2 g lysine per 100 g protein has been measured.* This value exceeds that found in high-lysine maize varieties (opaque-2 and floury-2) even in milk. It is about the same as that found in soymeal.

The seeds of all three species are high in protein. *Amaranthus hypochondriacus* seed contains about 15 percent protein and 63 percent starch. The starch is similar to the premium-priced starch of waxy maize.†

These amaranths are now cultivated as minor grain crops in Latin America: *Amaranthus caudatus* in the Andean regions of Argentina, Peru, and Bolivia; *Amaranthus cruentus* in Guatemala; and *Amaranthus hypochondriacus* in Mexico. They are ancient crops, which at the time of the Conquest were major grain crops in tropical highlands of the Americas. Displaced by larger-seeded grains such as maize, they were relegated to secondary, often inconspicuous, roles. Cultivation of *Amaranthus hypochondriacus* was also

*W. J. S. Downton. 1973. See Selected Readings.
†Ibid.

suppressed by the Spanish church in its effort to eradicate pagan Aztec ceremonies that centered around amaranths. For over a century, grain amaranths have been important to Asian hill tribes, and their use is spreading into the plains of India.

Amaranth grain is usually parched and milled and the dough formed into pancakes, or it may be cooked for gruel, popped and made into confections, or powdered and made into a drink. Young plants are often gathered as potherbs.

Although little accurate information is available on amaranth grain yield, the crop is reported to show a greater yield than maize grown on adjacent plots. A harvest of about 1 ton per hectare has been reported for *Amaranthus hypochondriacus* cultivated in Gujarat State in India.

## LIMITATIONS AND SPECIAL REQUIREMENTS

The amaranths grown for grain are pale seeded. The appearance, flavor, and popping capability of the pale seeds are best. Wild, dark-seeded varieties are those generally used as potherbs and ornamentals; they are not suitable for grain. Dark seeds should be culled before planting because they often produce vigorous, weedy plants.

Amaranths require good, well-tilled soil and moderate rainfall. Seed may be broadcast, and the seedlings thinned (thinnings make good potherbs), or transplanted out as nursery-grown plants. Each plant requires about as much room as a large maize plant. They probably require large amounts of nitrogen and phosphorus.

The huge seed heads must be cut when the seed begins to ripen and fall. Threshing and winnowing require hand labor.

Each of the three *Amaranthus* species grows in a wide range of climates, but local varieties differ in their day-length responses: experimentation is required to find varieties best suited to a given location.

## RESEARCH NEEDS

Because of the importance of the discovery of high lysine in *Amaranthus edulis*, the composition and nutritive potential of varieties of the other *Amaranthus* species should be evaluated by nutritionists.

Investigation of the preparation of the seed (and derived products) into acceptable dishes should be initiated. Processing losses and preservation methods for commercial and home use should be considered. Particular emphasis should be placed on labor requirements, rotation and cropping patterns, and comparisons with other crops grown in the same

The seed head of *Amaranthus hypochondriacus.* (Rodale Press, Inc.)

Harvesting heavily laden *Amaranthus hypochondriacus.* (Rodale Press, Inc.)

region. A detailed study of the traditional cultivation, harvesting, processing, and use of grain amaranths in Latin America and India's highland regions is necessary.

Since seed shedding (shattering) is a problem, an effort should be made to discover nonshattering varieties.

As in soybeans, the onset of grain amaranth flowering depends on day length (photoperiod). Races should be selected for different latitudes and rainfall regimes.

Accurate records of yield are needed for different agronomic treatments and in different climatic regions.

Seed size may have important influence on seed composition (for example, the ratio of husk to endosperm) and hence on seed quality. Seed size, therefore, warrants special agronomic attention.

## Selected Readings

Downton, W. J. S. 1973. *Amaranthus edulis*: a high lysine grain amaranth. *World Crops.* 25(1):20.
MacMasters, M. M., P. D. Baird, M. M. Hazapfel, and E. C. Rist. 1955. Preparation of starch from *Amaranthus cruentus* seed. *Economic Botany.* 9(3):300-2.
Safford, W. E. 1917. A forgotten cereal of ancient America. *Proceedings 19th International Congress of Americanists, 1915.* Washington, D.C. pp. 286-97.
Sauer, J. D. 1950. The grain amaranths: a survey of their history and classification. *Annals of the Missouri Botanical Garden.* 37: 561-632.
Sauer, J. D. 1967. The grain amaranths and their relatives; a revised taxonomic and geographic survey. *Annals of the Missouri Botanical Garden.* 54:103-37.
Singh, H. 1962. *Grain Amaranths, Buckwheat and Chenopods.* Indian Council of Agricultural Research, New Delhi.

## Research Contacts and Germ Plasm Supply

Asian Vegetable Research and Development Center, P.O. Box 42, Shanhua, Tainan, 741, Taiwan, Republic of China (J.A. Deutsch)
CSIRO, Division of Horticultural Research, Box 350, G.P.O. Adelaide, Australia 5001 (W.J.S. Downton)
Department of Agronomy, University of California, Davis, California 95616, USA ( R. S. Loomis and W.A. Williams)
Director, Human Nutrition Program, The University of Michigan, M5174 School of Public Health II, Ann Arbor, Michigan 48104, USA (J. R. K. Robson)
Indigenous Foods Consultants, Inc., 1885 Fuller Road, Ann Arbor, Michigan 48105, USA (J. Elias)
Institute of Agricultural Research, New Delhi, India
Rodale Press, 222 Main Street, Emmaus, Pennsylvania 18049, USA (A. Cunard)
Stanford University, Stanford, California 94305, USA (J. Frei)
The Close, 15 Cambridge Road, Girton, Cambridge CB3 OPN, England (C.L.A. Leakey and P. Goode)
University of California, Los Angeles, California 90024, USA (J. Sauer)

# QUINUA

A staple of the ancient Incas, and still a staple for millions, quinua* is virtually unknown outside the highlands of Bolivia, Chile, Ecuador, and Peru. Its grain, rich in protein and containing a good amino acid balance, may prove to be a better protein source than most of the true cereals.

In the high Andes, quinua is primarily a food of campesinos and poorer classes; increasing quinua production and use could improve their inadequate diet. In particular, the greater use of quinua in livestock feeds would result in better meat production. In highland tropical areas outside of the Andes quinua could prove valuable for improving nutrition, too.

Although long used for human consumption, quinua seeds have bitter tasting constituents—chiefly saponins. They are in the seed's outer layer and can be washed out in cold water. However, this method does not assure the uniform quality necessary for commercial distribution. Recently, Bolivian breeders have selected a saponin-free variety, but widespread testing is just beginning.

Quinua is a hardy plant; before the Spanish Conquest it was one of few native grains hardy enough for the high Andes. Subsequently, it was largely supplanted by barley—a less nutritious grain. An annual herb, quinua grows 1-2.5 m tall. It is cultivated at altitudes of 2,500-4,000 m where, with short day length, the plant matures in 5 or 6 months, producing an abundance of white or pink seeds in large sorghum-like clusters. These nutritious seeds contain 58 percent starch, 5 percent sugar, 12-19 percent protein, and 4-5 percent fat.

Quinua seeds are used in soup and ground into flour for bread and cake. They have also been used to make beer and produce feed for swine and poultry. A quinua breakfast cereal is manufactured in Peru and quinua has demonstrated value as a partial wheat-flour substitute for enriching bread. Quinua leaves are sometimes used as a green vegetable.

Although quinua grows in areas having short day length, cool climates, and high altitudes, it is possible that new varieties can be created for other latitudes and altitudes.

Work has been conducted in Peru and Bolivia on the biology of the plant. Races have been catalogued, variety and fertilizer trials have been conducted in various localities, and some strains have been selected. The Bolivian saponin-free variety (cross-bred and selected at the Patacamaya Experiment Station; see Contacts list page 23) is called *sajama.* It requires no washing, has shown no deleterious effects in food or animal feed, and is now being field tested in the Bolivian and Peruvian Altiplano.

*Chenopodium quinoa* Willd. Also known as quinoa. Family: Chenopodiaceae.

Quinua.
(A. Bacigalupo)

Harvesting quinua in Bolivia. (C. B. Heiser)

Two related *Chenopodium* species are also cultivated as food plants in the Americas: Cañihua *Chenopodium pallidicaule* and Huauzontle *Chenopodium nuttaliae*. Cañihua *Chenopodium pallidicaule* has an even higher protein content than quinua and grows at higher elevations in the Andes of Peru and Bolivia. It is a potential crop plant for extreme highlands in other parts of the world. However, it has low yield, is only a semi-domesticated plant, and will need much experimental work before it can fulfill its potential.

Huauzontle *Chenopodium nuttaliae* is cultivated in south central Mexico, at altitudes of 1,200-3,000 m, largely for its flower clusters (which are used as a vegetable), although several strains are grown as grains. Protein analyses of the available varieties should precede attempts to encourage wider cultivation. This species will hybridize with quinua, which suggests the possibility of improving both.

## LIMITATIONS AND SPECIAL REQUIREMENTS

No intensive research on quinua cultivation has been done: growing methods have changed imperceptibly during the past four centuries.

Saponins could be a blessing in disguise; their bitterness may deter those insects and birds that are normally pests in grain fields. Perhaps this is why strains containing saponins have prevailed.

If not removed, saponins adversely affect the taste and digestibility of quinua-based animal feeds.

Quinua varieties show highly variable protein content. The Patacamaya Experiment Station has varieties with 16, 17, 18, and 19 percent protein.

## RESEARCH NEEDS

Collection of seeds from all quinua varieties growing throughout the Andean region is necessary. Safely stored in a seed bank the seeds could provide the germ plasm needed for genetic improvement, for trials in new locations, and for implementation of an intensive plant-breeding program.

Initially, all races should be examined to find saponin-free, high-yield plants with large seeds, high protein content, and good amino-acid balance. A further requirement is identification of quinua varieties with the highest nutritive value for domestic animals.

Both intraspecific and interspecific cross-breeding should be attempted. In addition to the numerous races of cultivated quinua, wild or weedy types are also recognized (for example, *Chenopodium quinoa* var. *melanospermum*). Some of these weeds may offer useful genes (for example, for disease resistance). Hybrids between quinua and huauzontle show reduced fertility, but seed is produced; it should prove possible to transfer genes from one species to the other.

The effectiveness of saponins as a pest deterrent should be evaluated. It may be preferable (energetically and ecologically) to mill out the saponins after harvest rather than to apply pesticides during the growing season.

## Selected Readings

Bruin, A. de. 1964. Investigation of the food value of quinua and cañihua seed. *Journal of Food Science*. 29:872-6.

Cardozo, S., J. Rea, and I. A. de Viscarra. 1970. *Bibliografía de la Quinua y la Cañihua*, Boletín bibliográfico # 13. Sociedad de Ingenieros Agrónomos de Bolivia (La Paz).

Gade, D. W. 1970. Ethnobotany of cañihua (*Chenopodium pallidicaule*) rustic seed crop of the Andes. *Economic Botany*. 24:55-61.

Gandarillas, H. 1968. Carácteres botánicos mas importantes para la clasificación de la quinua. In *Convención de Quenopodiaceas*. Primera, Puno, Perú, Noviembre 5-8. Anales. Puno, Universidad, Facultad de Agronomia.

Gandarillas, H. 1968. *Estudios de Herencia de la Quinoa*. Boletín Experimental 35. Ministerio de Agricultura, Division de Investigaciones, Instituto Boliviano de Cultivos Andinos, La Paz, Bolivia.

Gandarillas, H. 1968. *Razas de Quinoa*. Boletín Experimental 34. Ministerio de Agricultura, Division de Investigaciones, Instituto Boliviano de Cultivos Andinos, La Paz, Bolivia.

León, J. 1964. *Plantas Alimenticias Andinas*. Boletín Técnico 6, Instituto Interamericano de Ciencias Agrícolas, Lima, Perú. (Probably the best general reference; has extensive bibliography.)

Nelson, D. C. 1968. Taxonomy and origins of *Chenopodium quinoa* and *Chenopodium nuttaliae*. Ph.D. Thesis, Indiana University (Available from University Microfilms, Ann Arbor, Michigan, USA. Order number 69-4792).

Simmonds, N. W. 1965. The grain chenopods of the tropical American highlands. *Economic Botany*. 19:223-34.

White, P. L., E. Alvistur, C. Dias, E. Vinas, H. S. White, and C. Collazos. 1955. Nutrient content and protein quality of quinua and cañihua, edible seed products of the Andes mountains. *Journal of Agricultural Food Chemistry*. 3:531-5.

Wilson, H. D. 1974. Experimental hybridization of the cultivated chenopods (*Chenopodium* L.) and wild relatives. *Proceedings of the Indiana Academy of Science (Abstract) 82*. Available from author, address below.

## Research Contacts and Germ Plasm Supply

Department of Agronomy, Bradfield and Emerson Halls, Cornell University, Ithaca, New York 14850, USA (H. A. MacDonald)

Department of Plant Sciences, Indiana University, Bloomington, Indiana 47401, USA (H. D. Wilson)

Direccion de Investigacion Agropecuas, Ministerio de Agricultura, Apartado 2791, Lima, Peru (A. Bacigalupo)

Direccion General de Desarrollo Agropecuario, Apartado 309, Tegucigalpa, Honduras (Id. Gandarillas)

FAO, Via delle Terme di Caracalla, 00100, Rome, Italy (J. Leon)

Ministerio de Agricultura, La Paz, Bolivia

Patacamaya Experiment Station, Lavoratorio Experimental de Ciencias Cosmicas, Universidad Boliviana Mayor de San Andres, 1995 Av. Villazon, La Paz, Bolivia

Programa de Cereals, Universidad Nacional Agraria, La Molina, Lima, Perú

Universidad Nacional Agraria La Molina, Apartado 456, Lima, Perú (J. de Albertis and M. Romero Loli)

Universidad Tecnica del Altiplano, Puno, Perú (M. E. Tapia)

# ZOSTERA MARINA

*Zostera marina** is a marine flowering plant that grows in shallow seawater. It is one of the few plants that grow and flower fully submerged in seawater. When ripe, the grain-bearing part breaks loose and floats to the surface where it drifts to the shore and can then be harvested. Although little is known about the use of *Zostera marina* as a grain crop, it yields well in warm, clear, sun-drenched water. It holds potential as a food crop that can be grown in tropical estuaries around the world. However, almost nothing is known about *Zostera marina* as a crop plant and only exploratory, small-scale research is warranted at present.

The only recorded case in which the sea has been used for grain production is that of the *Zostera marina* harvested by Seri Indians on the West Coast of Mexico.[†] The Seri Indians prepared *Zostera marina* grain by threshing sun-dried plants with wooden clubs and loosening the fruit by rolling the seed heads between their palms. The product was winnowed (tossed in the air), then the grain was toasted, rewinnowed, and ground into flour. Cooked in water into a thick or thin gruel, the flour has a bland flavor. Traditionally it was combined with other food, usually sea turtle oil or honey.

The plant is native to the coasts of the northern hemisphere from the subarctic to the subtropic. Related species occur in the southern hemisphere.

The grain derived from *Zostera marina* is 3-3.5 mm long and 1-1.5 mm in diameter. Like wheat flour, *Zostera* grain flour is relatively bland and can be variously flavored. The one sample analyzed to date shows its protein and starch contents compare favorably with those of wheat, rice, and other grains: 13.2 percent protein, 50.9 percent starch, and 1.0 percent crude fat.

The leaves of *Zostera marina* may also prove valuable as fodder, thatching, or packing material. The foliage is an important food for some sea turtles and water fowl. An important shallow-water, mud-flat stabilizer, the plant helps to sustain the productivity of estuarine and other coastal areas.

## LIMITATIONS AND SPECIAL REQUIREMENTS

Though transplantation and seeding experiments are under way, and some previous cultivation work exists, little is known about the propagation or production of these plants as a crop. Even among the Seri Indians, only the elderly know about its traditional use within the tribe. Thus, even the limitations and special requirements of this plant are now unknown.

*Zostera marina*. Also known as eelgrass. Family: Potamogetonaceae.
†Felger and Moser, 1973. See Selected Readings.

*Zostera marina.* (C. P. McRoy)

The grain from *Zostera marina*. (C. P. McRoy)

A Seri Indian woman at El Desemboque, Sonora, Mexico, winnowing the grain from *Zostera marina* harvested from the sea nearby. (R. S. Felger)

## RESEARCH NEEDS

Research on both harvesting procedures and nutritional analysis and use of *Zostera marina* seeds is needed. Large-scale collections should be made for analysis and general experimentation.

Attention should be given to the temperature tolerance and day-length requirements of varieties from different areas. Attention should also be given to certain vigorous, wide-leafed varieties, which may produce higher yields.

## Selected Readings

Felger, R. S. 1975. Nutritionally significant new crops for arid lands: a model from the Sonoran desert. In *Priorities in Child Nutrition in Developing Countries*, ed. Jean Mayer. Vol. II, Section 16. United Nations Children's Fund, New York. (Order Number: E/ICEF/L.1328.)

Felger, R. S., and C. P. McRoy. 1975. Seagrasses as potential food plants. In *Seedbearing Halophytes as Food Plants: Proceedings of a Conference*, ed. C. Fred Somers. Del-SG-3-75. pp. 62-9. College of Marine Studies, University of Delaware, Newark, Delaware, USA.

Felger, R. S., and M. B. Moser. 1973. Eelgrass (*Zostera marina* L.) in the Gulf of California: Discovery of its nutritional value by the Seri Indians. *Science*. 181:355-6.

den Hartog, C. 1970. *The Sea Grasses of the World*. North-Holland Publishing Company, Amsterdam.

McRoy, C. P., and R. C. Phillips. 1968. Supplementary bibliography on eelgrass, *Zostera marina*. *U.S. Fish and Wildlife Service Special Science Report Wildlife 114*. Government Printing Office, Washington, D.C., USA.

Phillips, R. C. 1964. Comprehensive bibliography of *Zostera marina*. *U.S. Fish and Wildlife Service Special Science Report Wildlife 79*. Government Printing Office, Washington, D.C., USA.

## Research Contacts and Germ Plasm Supply

Arizona-Sonora Desert Museum, P.O. Box 5607, Tucson, Arizona 85715, USA (R. S. Felger)

Department of Botany, Seattle Pacific College, Seattle, Washington 98119, USA (R. C. Phillips)

Institute of Marine Science, University of Alaska, Fairbanks, Alaska 99701 (C. P. McRoy)

# II ROOTS AND TUBERS

## ARRACACHA

Native to the Andean highlands from Venezuela to Bolivia, arracacha* is an herbaceous perennial that produces large, thick, edible, carrot-shaped, starchy roots with a color suggesting parsnip. Arracacha is cultivated today in most Latin American countries as far north as Costa Rica, usually in small gardens for local use. In the larger cities of Colombia, however, arracacha roots are sold in considerable quantities. In many areas arracacha replaces the potato; it costs only half as much to plant and harvest.

If introduced into other high-altitude areas of the tropics, arracacha is likely to be a valuable root crop, particularly if improved cultivars and cultural techniques are developed. The tubers are reported to have a starch content ranging from about 10 to 25 percent and to be rich in calcium and phosphorus. The starch is similar in many respects to that of cassava; it is easily digested and can be used in infant and invalid foods. It also makes a suitable laundry starch.

Secondary tubers (offshoots of the main tuber) are an important carbohydrate foodstuff and are boiled or fried as a table vegetable or used as an ingredient in stews. They have a delicate flavor, a crisp texture, and, depending on the cultivar, white, creamy-yellow, or purple flesh. In many areas yellow tubers are preferred.

All other parts of the plant are also used: offsets for the next planting, the coarse main rootstocks and mature leaves for livestock feeding, young stems for salads or a table vegetable.

Arracacha thrives in any good soil and is cultivated like, and often interplanted with, potatoes. The secondary tubers usually mature 10-14 months after planting; sometimes an early harvest of immature roots is taken after about 4-8 months. The entire plants are pulled up with the roots attached.

Seeds are seldom produced; propagation is entirely vegetative. Planting can be done at any time, but is usually done at the beginning of the rainy season.

*Arracacia xanthorrhiza* Bancroft. Family: Umbelliferae. Also known as Peruvian carrot, arracha, Peruvian parsnip, and *Arracacia esculenta* DC.

A Colombian farmer among rows of arracacha, a crop for highland regions. (F. Higuitia Muñoz)

Arracacha: The roots are ready for market. (F. Higuitia Muñoz)

In Colombia, arracacha is sold in sacks, 60 kg each. (F. Higuitia Muñoz)

## LIMITATIONS AND SPECIAL REQUIREMENTS

Except in the lowlands, arracacha yields at all elevations in the Andes. It requires a moderate, evenly distributed rainfall of at least 60 cm (but preferably 100 cm); if the natural rainfall is insufficient, supplementary irrigation is required. For optimum results an equable temperature of 15-20°C throughout the year is needed. There are some varieties—those normally grown at lower elevations—that are frost sensitive, but the varieties adapted to the higher altitudes, where they do get occasional and light frosts, appear not to be seriously harmed by them.

In some regions arracacha is susceptible to nematode attack, but this can be controlled successfully with a copper-based pesticide.

Harvesting cannot be delayed because roots left in the ground become fibrous and tough and develop a strong, unpleasant flavor. Because of a short shelf life, it can be a relatively high-priced product in the marketplace.

## RESEARCH NEEDS

Arracacha cultivation should be tested in the highlands and hill country of East Africa, Central Africa, India, Southeast Asia, New Guinea, etc. Some remnants of old introductions may still exist in the highlands of Central America (e.g., Guatemala) and the West Indies (Jamaica, Cuba, and Puerto Rico); local agronomists should investigate. Given some research attention the remnants may provide material for arracacha improvement and expansion.

Little direct testing of the environmental tolerances of arracacha has been conducted; study of the latitude, altitude, temperature, soil type, and moisture requirements is needed. A study of pathogens infecting arracacha should also be made.

Three varieties of cultivated arracacha (distinguished mainly by the color of the flesh of the roots) are known. Wild varieties may exist in the Andean region; they should be sought and preserved. No analysis of the relative nutritional and agronomic merits of even the existing varieties has been done. Research on this is needed.

### Selected Readings

Constance, L. 1959. The South American species of *Arracacia* (Umbelliferae) and some related genera. *Torrey Botanical Club Bulletin*. 76:39-52.

Hodge, W. H. 1954. The edible Arracacha—a little known root crop of the Andes. *Economic Botany*. 8(3):195-221.

Higuitia Muñóz, F. 1968. El cultivo de la arracacha en la sabana de Bogotá. *Agricultura Tropical*. 24(3):139-46.

Higuitia Muñóz, F. 1969. Comparative yield of nine varieties of *Arracacia xanthorrhiza*. *Agricultura Tropical*. 25(9):566-70. *Field Crop Abstracts*. 24(1):1015.

León, J. 1967. Andean tuber and root crops: origins and variability. *Proceedings First International Symposium. Tropical Root Crops, 1 Pt.* 1:121.

Kay, D. E. 1973. *TPI Crop and Product Digest No. 2: Root Crops*. Tropical Products Institute, London. (Available from Publications Section, Tropical Products Institute, 56/62 Gray's Inn Road, London WC1X 8LU, England. Price £1.50 plus postage.)

### Research Contacts and Germ Plasm Supply

Botanical Museum, Harvard University, Oxford Street, Cambridge, Massachusetts 02138, USA (R. E. Schultes)

Department of Botany, Indiana University, Bloomington, Indiana 61701, USA (C. Heiser)

Instituto de Ciencias Naturales de la Universidad Nacional, Apartado 2535, Bogotá, Colombia (A. Fernández-Pérez)

L. H. Bailey Hortorium, Cornell University, Ithaca, New York 14850, USA (W. Hodge)

# COCOYAMS

Great effort has been devoted to introducing and adapting the potato to the lowland tropics, while indigenous tropical root crops have been largely neglected. Cocoyams,* native to the Americas, are already adapted to tropical conditions and have been successfully introduced to other tropical regions, especially West Africa. There are about 30-40 cocoyam species growing randomly throughout the tropics, but only five or six are important sources of edible products. Despite their adaptability, acceptance, and commercial food value, cocoyams have received little attention by researchers. Consequently, their potential is not being realized, and their use is declining.

Much of the potential of cocoyams lies in commercial (rather than subsistence) production. If agronomists select high-yield, good-quality cultivars, and develop a technology for their intensive cultivation, cocoyams could become a major tropical food crop. Their future depends particularly on reducing production costs, possibly by mechanizing some of the cultural practices.

Cocoyams have a central tuberous root (corm) surrounded by smaller potato-sized tubers (cormels). Only the cormels are normally used for human consumption. The corms are used for animal feed and for replanting. Capable of yielding 30-60 tons of cormels per ha, cocoyams can be grown in various types of soil. Like potatoes, the cormels may be boiled, baked, parboiled, fried in oil, or ground into flour. In West Africa, fresh tubers are ground (to produce *fufu*) and used to thicken stews and soups.

The cormels compare with potatoes in nutritive value. They contain 2-3 percent protein (fresh weight) but are deficient in lysine, methionine and cysteine. Rich in minerals and vitamins, they are palatable energy foods. The tender leaves and shoots are a nutritious, spinach-like vegetable.

Some cocoyam varieties yield a cormel crop in as little as 3 months, others in 10 months. Cormels can be harvested individually as each matures, or they can be left until all mature and then harvested simultaneously. Some cultivars (in fairly dry soil) can be left in place for as long as 2 years without the cormels deteriorating. Harvested cormels can be stored in a cool, dry place for 2-3 months with little effect on quality.

Cocoyams grow best at low to medium altitudes in the humid (frost-free) tropics. Riverine land, too wet for sweet potatoes and yams, is well suited for cocoyams. Some varieties, however, also grow well in dry soils. For optimum yields they require deep, well-drained, rich soil and 140-200 mm of rain, well

---

*Xanthosoma sagittifolium, Xanthosoma violaceum, Xanthosoma brasiliense, Xanthosoma atrovirens. Also known as tania, tanier, yautia, new cocoyam, etc. Family: Araceae.

distributed throughout the year. In areas where the rainfall is inadequate they can be grown under irrigation.

Cocoyams can be grown within a wide temperature range, but do best in an average annual temperature of about 24°C. They are relatively disease- and pest-free. The most common diseases are soft-rot and root-rot. Care must be taken to avoid bruising the tubers during harvest; otherwise they are liable to rot in storage.

## LIMITATIONS AND SPECIAL REQUIREMENTS

Because virus diseases can devastate root crops, extreme caution should be exercised and quarantine enforced when cocoyams are introduced to new areas.

Cocoyams require abundant and well-distributed rainfall. Where prolonged droughts occur they are not likely to flourish unless irrigated.

Like most root crops, cocoyams have specific soil requirements.

Cocoyam roots and the edible corms that surround them. Individual corms can be harvested (as shown here by the stump visible in the center of the roots) leaving the plant in the ground for the others to mature. (D. L. Plucknett)

Cocoyams approaching maturity in a small rural farm in Nigeria. (D. L. Plucknett)

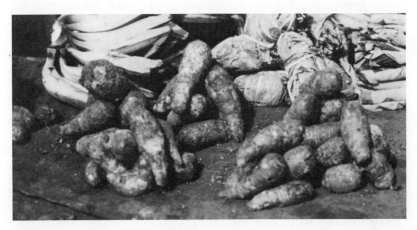

Cocoyam corms in a village market in Ghana. Cocoyam is suited to small-farmer production in rural areas. (E. S. Ayensu)

In commercial ventures, where cocoyams are grown under mass cultivation, pest and disease problems can be expected to increase in severity.

## RESEARCH NEEDS

Many cocoyam varieties exist and they differ widely in yield, adaptation to soils and climate, plant characteristics, corm size, palatability, and starch content. Such varieties must be collected from many tropical regions and their food potential determined.

Superior varieties should be field tested together (under quarantine) to determine performance and cormel quality. With the genetic variability available, and the simplicity of clonal selection, varieties with increased yield and quality and higher protein levels must be selected.

Many (or most) cocoyam plants are infected by virus. Although not fatal to the plant, the infection does reduce yield. The virus is found in the corms and cormels, so planting them transmits the virus. But reproducing cocoyams by seed—generally thought to be impossible but recently shown by researchers at the University of Florida (see address below) to be eminently feasible—produces new plants that are virus free. The modern technique of tissue culture also promises to remove the infection. Once virus-free cocoyams are obtained, a certification program and strict quarantine will be needed to avoid reinfection.

Other agronomic factors requiring research are spacing, fertilizer, soil and water requirements, pest and weed control, and a complete study of the physiology of tuber formation.

Nutritional research is also needed because nothing is known about the biological value of cocoyam protein or the digestibility of the starch.

Research is needed to industrialize cocoyam products. The feasibility of producing fried cocoyam chips and flour on a commercial scale should be investigated.

## Selected Readings

Abruña-Rodrígues, F., E. G. Boneta-García, and J. Vicente-Chandler. 1967. Experiments on tanier production with conservation in Puerto Rico's mountain region. *Journal of Agriculture, University of Puerto Rico.* 51(2):167-75. (Available from The Agriculture Experiment Station, Rio Piedras, Puerto Rico.)

Coursey, D. G. 1968. The edible aroids. *World Crops.* 20(4):25-30.

Coursey, D. G., and P. H. Haynes. 1970. Root crops and their potential as food in the tropics. *World Crops.* 22(4):261.

de Albuquerque, M., and E. Pinheiro. 1970. Buerosas Feculantas. Serie: *Fitotecnia.* 1(3):33-47. Instituto de Pesquisas e Experimentacao Agropecuarias do Norte. (Now: Centro de Recuros Naturais de Amazónia, Belém, Pará, Brazil.)

Irvine, F. D. 1969. Xanthosoma. In *West African Agriculture* 3rd Ed. Vol. 2: *West African Crops.* pp. 177-9. Oxford University Press, London.

Karikari, S. K. 1971. Cocoyam cultivation in Ghana. *World Crops.* 23(3):118-22.

Kay, D. E. 1973. *TPI Crop and Product Digest No. 2: Root Crops.* Tropical Product Institute, London. (Available from: Publications Section, Tropical Products Institute, 56/62 Gray's Inn Road, London WC1X 8LU, England. Price £1.50 plus postage.)

Morton, J. F. 1972. Cocoyams (*Xanthosoma caracu, X. atrovirens,* and *X. nigrens*), ancient root and leaf vegetables gaining in economic importance. *Proceedings of Florida State Horticulture Society* 85:85-94.

Praquin, J. Y., and H. C. Miche. 1971. *Essai de conservation de taros et macabos au Cameroun.* Institut Recherche Agronomique Tropicales Rapport prelim No. 1. Dschang Station, Cameroon.

Winters, H. F., and G. W. Miskimen. 1967. *Vegetable Gardening in the Caribbean Area.* Agriculture Handbook No. 323. pp. 77-79. U.S. Department of Agriculture, Agriculture Research Service, Washington, D.C., USA.

### Research Contacts and Germ Plasm Supply

Agriculture Research and Education Center, University of Florida, 18905 SW. 280 St., Homestead, Florida 33030, USA (R. B. Volin)

Agricultural Experiment Station, Rio Piedras, Puerto Rico (J. Vicente-Chandler)

Department of Plant Pathology, University of Florida, Gainesville, Florida 32611, USA (F. W. Zettler).

Mayagüez Institute of Tropical Agriculture, Mayagüez, Puerto Rico 00708 (F. Martin).

University of the West Indies, St. Augustine, Trinidad (J. A. Spence).

# TARO

The taro* is widely grown; its tuberous roots are rich in starch and, like potatoes, can be boiled, baked, roasted, or fried in oil. However, only in Egypt, the Philippines, Hawaii, and certain other Pacific and Caribbean islands is the taro a commercial crop. With increased research and commercialization in the rest of the tropics, taro, with its exceptional yields and year-round production, could help overcome food shortages. It has particular potential for marshy, waterlogged regions and for coastal and salinified regions (because some cultivars are highly salt tolerant).

Underground, taro usually has one central corm and 6-20 spherical cormels around it. Both corm and cormels are eaten. They are often used as rice substitutes in Pacific and Asian countries. From the flesh, which is usually mealy and has a delicate, nutty flavor, a flour similar to potato flour can be produced for soups, biscuits, bread, beverages, and puddings. Easily digested, taro starch can be used in baby foods, hypoallergenic foods, and as a cereal substitute in diets for victims of celiac disease. In Hawaii, taro is made into *poi*—a paste made from boiled, mashed corms fermented a day or so. It is also sliced and fried into taro chips.

Low in protein and fat, taro is essentially a carbohydrate food. Nutritionally it compares favorably with other root crops—cassava, yams,

*Colocasia esculenta* (L.) Schott (sometimes called *Colocasia antiquorum.*) Also known as old cocoyam, dasheen, malanga, tania, tanier, tanyah, elephant ear. Family: Araceae.

Taro corm surrounded by the edible tubers. The variety shown here is the dasheen. (U. S. Department of Agriculture)

Irish potato, sweet potato—and with cereal crops, especially rice. It is a good source of minerals: calcium, phosphorus, and vitamins A and B. Taro leaves and petioles can be cooked and eaten like spinach. They provide protein, calcium, phosphorus, iron, potassium, and vitamins A, B, and C.

Taros are adapted to flooded environments and, like rice, can be grown in paddy culture. Under paddy they are grown in all soil types. They grow rapidly if fertility and water levels are maintained; the corms mature 6-18 months after planting.

Taro garden, western Samoa. Here the crop is being grown under dry-land conditions. (D. L. Plucknett)

In marshy areas such as this in Hawaii, taro is grown like rice under flooded paddy conditions. (D. L. Plucknett)

Taro can also be grown in dry, upland areas if water is provided by irrigation or by rainfall (mulching may be needed to maintain high soil moisture). Grown "dry" the best results are obtained on deep, well-drained, friable (particularly alluvial) loams.

The plant responds well to intensive agriculture: land preparation, planting, and harvesting can take place during all seasons. A field may often have taro plants in various stages of maturity, and the grower can also sell them year-round as they mature.

After harvest the tubers can be stored for up to 3 months, depending on variety.

In Hawaii taros have a high and profitable yield. In the island of Kauai, 2.14 million kg of corms have been produced from only 69 ha. In 1969, the prices paid for raw corms ranged from 17 to 20 cents/kg. From an average yield of 22,400 kg/ha the gross income per ha was almost $4,000.*

Several taro types, characterized by numerous, symmetrical, smaller tubers called dasheens, are grown in dry-land agriculture. Although popular in China, Japan, and among Asians throughout the tropics, dasheens are largely neglected plants. With high yields, high nutritive value, and superior keeping quality, they have great unrealized potential. Grown either rain fed or irrigated, dasheens mature more rapidly than paddy-grown taro—and yield less. They grow best in loose, water-retentive, clay soils. Usually planted at the beginning of the rainy season, they can, if carefully managed, be produced year-round. Dasheen shoots are highly prized by the Japanese and, if canned, they offer tropical countries a good export potential.

## LIMITATIONS AND SPECIAL REQUIREMENTS

Transporting taro root germ plasm throughout the world is dangerous. It can spread phytopathogens, which severely decrease yield, to new areas. For example, the virus diseases and the taro leaf hopper, *Tarophagus proserpina* Kirkaldy, that transmits them, occur in New Britain and the British Solomon Islands. Importing germ plasm from those islands must be avoided at all costs.

Taro growing requires intensive effort. It calls for manual labor and long hours of work in muddy, flooded fields; consequently its production is decreasing.

With all the variation available it is essential to select the appropriate variety for the specific location. For optimum results taros require hot, humid conditions, with daily average temperatures of 21-27°C. In more temperate areas, or at high altitudes, there must be a 6-7 month frost-free period.

*Plucknett and de la Peña. 1971. See Selected Readings.

Water control is absolutely necessary. Upland taros and dasheens require well-distributed, year-round rainfall (or substitute irrigation) and a long growing season.

If stored, corms must be kept dry and injury free. Dasheens can be stored at 10°C for up to 6 months. In Egypt taros are stored at 7°C for more than 3 months at a time. Solomon Islands taro corms cannot be stored; decay begins within a week of harvest.

## RESEARCH NEEDS

Phytopathogens such as dasheen mosaic virus are widespread among taro. Removing the pathogens will give an immediate increase in yield. Reproducing taro by planting corms and cormels also transmits the infection, but two avenues promise to produce virus-free plants—tissue culture and reproduction via seeds. Taro tissue culture has been successfully accomplished in Hawaii and offers hope for clearing cultivars of viruses. Though taro will flower and set seed, there has never been a breeding program either for removing pathogens or for genetic improvement. Once pathogen-free taro is

Peeling taro, western Samoa. (D. L. Plucknett)

obtained, a certification program and strict quarantine will be required to maintain it.

In Hawaii, taro and dasheen varieties are well known, and production techniques well developed. The U.S. organizations that fund technical assistance should support efforts to distribute varieties and disseminate information about taros and dasheens throughout the tropics.

Taro production must be modernized: mechanization, crop management systems, and weed control are the most critical needs. Mechanization in the paddy environment offers engineers a great challenge. Mechanical methods for planting taro are badly needed. Planting on ridges is a possibility (it also simplifies water control and harvesting). Mechanical harvesting is even more challenging. Ultimately it may prove necessary to drain and dry the fields before mechanical harvest. Adapting small, hand-propelled rice cultivators has brought some progress in mechanization to Hawaii.* Upland taro mechanization is in its early stages, but it can be done (on a plantation scale) using modified tomato transplanters and potato diggers.

Research on virus diseases of taro is critical. The virulent virus in New Britain and the Solomon Islands is under study (at Malaita; see Research Contacts), but increased support and effort is essential to prevent its spread to new areas.

The pathogens responsible for decay of stored corms have been identified; research is needed on the use of fungicides and other methods to combat them.

The development of processed taro food products that could be used in hypoallergenic specialty foods would stimulate interest in the crop.

Basic botanic and agronomic knowledge of dasheens is inadequate. Much more research is warranted. Collection and evaluation of dasheen varieties would be an important first step. Cultivars must be collected and conserved to prevent their loss.

## Selected Readings

Barrau, J. 1953. Taro (an annotated bibliography). *South Pacific Commission Quarterly Bulletin.* 3(4):31-2.

Gooding, M. J., and J. S. Campbell. 1961. The improvement of cultivation methods in dasheen and eddoe (*Colocasia esculenta*) growing in Trinidad. *Proceedings of the American Horticultural Society, Caribbean Region.* 5:6-20.

Greenwell, A. B. H. 1947. Taro—with special reference to its culture and use in Hawaii. *Economic Botany.* 1(3):276-89.

Hodge, W. H. 1954. *The Dasheen, a Tropical Root Crop for the South.* U.S. Department of Agriculture Circular No. 950. U.S. Department of Agriculture, Washington, D.C., USA.

*Plucknett *et al.* 1970. See Selected Readings.

Jackson, G. V. H., and D. E. Gollifer. 1975. Disease and Pest Problems of Taro (*Colocasia esculenta* L. Schott) in the British Solomon Islands. *PANS.* 21(1):45-53.

Kay, D. E. 1973. *TPI Crop and Product Digest No. 2: Root Crops.* Tropical Products Institute, London. (Available from: Publications Section, Tropical Products Institute, 56/62 Gray's Inn Road, London WC1X 8LU, England. Price £1.50 plus postage.)

Miller, C. D. 1927. *Food Values of Poi, Taro, and Limu.* Hawaii Agricultural Experiment Station Bulletin 78. University of Hawaii, Honolulu, Hawaii.

Plucknett, D. L., R. S. de la Peña, and R. Obrero. 1970. Taro (*Colocasia esculenta*). *Field Crops Abstracts.* 23(4):413-26.

Plucknett, D. L., and R. S. de la Peña. 1971. Taro production in Hawaii. *World Crops.* 23(5):244-9.

Plucknett, D. L., H. C. Ezuman, and R. S. de la Peña. Mechanization of taro culture in Hawaii. *Proceedings, 3rd International Symposium on Tropical Root and Tuber Crops, Nigeria.* (In Press)

Tisbe, V. O., and T. G. Cadiz. 1967. Corm and root crops: taro or gabi. In: *Vegetable Production in Southeast Asia.* Eds., J. E. Knot and J. R. Deanon, Jr. pp. 293-300. Los Banos University of the Philippines, College of Agriculture, Laguna, Philippines.

Whitney, L. D., F. I. A. Bowers, and M. Takahashi. 1939. *Taro Varieties in Hawaii.* Hawaii Agricultural Experiment Station Bulletin 84. University of Hawaii, Honolulu, Hawaii.

## Research Contacts and Germ Plasm Supply

Agricultural Research and Education Center, University of Florida, 18905 SW 280 St., Homestead, Florida 33030, USA (R. B. Volin)

Dala Research Station, Malaita, British Solomon Islands (G. V. H. Jackson and D. Gollifer)

Department of Agriculture, Suva, Fiji (P. Sivan)

Department of Agronomy and Soil Science, College of Tropical Agriculture, University of Hawaii, Honolulu, Hawaii 96822, USA (D. L. Plucknett)

Department of Plant Pathology, University of Florida, Gainesville, Florida 32611, USA (F. W. Zettler)

International Institute of Tropical Agriculture, P.M.B. 5320, Ibadan, Nigeria (H. S. Ezumah)

Kauai Branch Station, Kapaa, Kauai, Hawaii 96746, USA (R. S. de la Peña)

Lyon Arboretum, University of Hawaii, Honolulu, Hawaii 96822, USA

Mayagüez Institute of Tropical Agriculture, Mayagüez, Puerto Rico 00708 (F. Martin)

Plant Pathology Department, Rothamsted Experimental Station, Harpenden, Herts, England AL5 2JQ (A. J. Kabek)

South Pacific Regional College of Tropical Agriculture, Apia, Western Samoa (W. Cable)

# III VEGETABLES

## CHAYA

Chaya,* a fast-growing ornamental and shade shrub, is a source of nutritious green leaves and shoots. It requires little maintenance (for example, the soil around it does not need tilling) and produces large amounts of greenery for years. A few plants grown experimentally in Puerto Rico have outgrown and outproduced all other leafy vegetables.

The attractive shrubs, 3-5 m tall, are often seen as hedges in Mexico and Honduras. Native chaya grows in thickets or open forest (often in rocky places) at altitudes up to 1,300 m. There are two forms: *Cnidoscolus aconitifolius* is found in native dooryards from southern Mexico to Costa Rica; *Cnidoscolus chayamansa* is grown as a hedge or dooryard plant in the Yucatan peninsula of Mexico and in British Honduras. *Cnidoscolus chayamansa* is occasionally grown in Florida and Cuba, but seems not to have been disseminated to other regions.

Chaya's young shoots and tender leaves are cooked and eaten like spinach. Reportedly they are high in protein, calcium, iron, carotene, thiamine, riboflavin, niacin, and ascorbic acid. They are probably suitable for canning or freezing for local and export markets, but this has not yet been attempted.

So far, chaya appears free of the pests and diseases that plague green garden vegetables in tropical climates, an important economic and ecological advantage. However, horn worms can rapidly defoliate it (but the plants quickly recover their leaves).

Chaya is propagated from stem cuttings, and woody stem sections germinate readily. Edible greenery is produced within 2 or 3 months. Because of the softness of the wood, the plant is easily pruned and maintained within reach of the ground. The plants tolerate heavy rainfall and respond with luxurious growth. Drought is also tolerated, and plants recover well when the rain returns.

*Cnidoscolus chayamansa* McVaugh and *Cnidoscolus aconitifolius*. Also known as tree spinach. Family: Euphorbiaceae.

45

Freshly plucked chaya leaves. Before being eaten they are boiled in water and become tender, but chewy. (J. Morton)

## LIMITATIONS AND SPECIAL REQUIREMENTS

The horticulture of chaya has never been studied.

The plants vary from smooth to hairy, and the hairy plants sting like nettles, so that harvesters must wear gloves. The stinging disappears with cooking. Cultivated plants are almost free of stinging hairs; it is likely that this is the result of long years of selection by the harvesters.

Chaya must be cooked before eating: the fresh leaves contain toxic hydrocyanic glycosides, but cooking inactivates them.

Chaya grows prodigiously and can reach a height of more than six feet. This single plant is just three years old. (F. Martin)

## RESEARCH NEEDS

Experimental plantings of cuttings of *Cnidoscolus chayamansa* (the less hairy of the two species) should be established, and those plants selected that have a minimum of hairs and contain a minimum of hydrocyanic glycosides.

Bioassays should be undertaken to verify the apparent wholesomeness of this vegetable—special attention should be paid to the toxins.

Trial plantings should be made to determine yield per hectare, labor requirements, and other factors bearing on the feasibility of commercial production.

Investigations should be made into the potential for processing and marketing the product—fresh, canned, or quick-frozen.

Cuttings should be distributed for testing in tropical areas outside its native home.

## Selected Readings

Berlin, B., D. E. Breedlove, and P. H. Raven. 1974. *Principles of Tzeltal Plant Classification*. Academic Press, New York and London.

McVaugh, R. 1944. The genus *Cnidoscolus*: generic limits and intrageneric groups. *Bulletin Torrey Botanical Club*. 71(5):457-74.

Munsell, H. E. et al. 1949. Composition of food plants of Central America. I—Honduras. *Food Research*. 14(2):144-64.

Souza-Novelo, N. 1950. *Plantas Alimentícias y Plantas de Condimento que Viven en Yucatán*. Instituto Técnico Agrícola Henequenero, Mérida, Mexico, pp. 101-4.

Standley, P. C., and J. A. Steyermark. 1949. Flora of Guatemala. *Fieldiana Botany*. 24(6):59-60. Field Museum of Natural History, Chicago, Illinois, USA.

## Research Contacts and Germ Plasm Supply

Colegio de Postgraduados, Escuela Nacional de Agricultura, Chapingo Texcoco, Mexico (E. Hernández X)

Fairchild Tropical Garden, 10901 Old Cutler Road, Coral Gables, Florida 33156, USA (J. Popenoe)

Mayagüez Institute of Tropical Agriculture, Mayagüez, Puerto Rico 00708

Oficina de Asesoria Técnica, Edificio "Centroamericana," 7A, Avenida 7-78, Zona 4, Oficina 605, Guatemala, Guatemala, Central America (J. Colína Campollo)

# HEARTS OF PALM

There is an increasing market throughout the world for expensive, exotic, foods; an example is the growing demand for palm hearts.* A tropical delicacy, palm hearts are the growing tips of palm trees. Reminiscent of artichoke hearts, they may be added to salads, served as a vegetable, or used to enhance the flavor of other vegetables. Although the demand for palm hearts is larger than the supply, little awareness of their commercial potential exists outside Brazil and Costa Rica.

World consumption increases daily. Brazil's abundance of wild palms has long been utilized, but rising demand is threatening their extinction: to obtain the heart, the tree must be killed.

Cultivation of palm trees for palm hearts is long overdue. Cultivation offers a practical way to circumvent forest destruction and to preserve existing stands. Rising labor costs and the increasing difficulty of harvesting

*Also known as palm cabbage and palmitos.

Many palms can be used as a source of hearts of palm. This is *Euterpe edulis*, which, in Brazil, is widely harvested for this purpose. The "heart" is inside the smooth portion of the stem, visible here between the fruit clusters and the leaves. (W. H. Hodge)

the thinning wild stands provide economic incentives for plantation culture. In Brazil, replanting is already mandatory, and cultivation is being encouraged.

The palm heart is a cylindrical bundle of leaf bases. The heart may be several inches in diameter and several feet long. Its composition and food value is similar to that of cabbage (*Brassica*).

The possibilities of establishing palm hearts as a plantation crop are good. Fast growing palms, well suited for this purpose, are recognized, and other potential species are abundant. A few, such as pejibaye (*Guilielma gasipaes*; see page 73), produce several stems emerging from a common root cluster, so that only one stem, not a whole plant, is sacrificed to harvest the heart.

In the past, palm hearts have been harvested entirely from wild specimens of *Euterpe*, *Prestoea*, *Guilielma*, *Roystonea*, *Sabal*, *Acrocomia*, and other palms in tropical America and the West Indies. Brazil is the principal supplier of canned palm hearts for the North American market. Brazilian assaí palms (*Euterpe edulis* Mart.), both wild and cultivated, have been a source of palm hearts since the mid-1960s. In the past few years in Costa Rica, pejibaye

The heart of a palm.  (R. W. Read)

palm has been set out in plantations for the production of palm hearts. When the seedlings are 3½ years old, the hearts are harvested and canned. It is reported that other potential commercial palms are *Sabal* spp., *Euterpe oleracea* Mart., *Caryota* spp., and the coconut palm *Cocos nucifera* L.

Canned hearts of palm are widely exported.  (W. H. Hodge)

*Euterpe* and pejibaye are common in humid tropical forests of South America. *Euterpe* also grows in the West Indies, while coconut thrives on tropical coasts and neighboring inland regions of the northern and southern hemispheres. *Caryota* spp. are common in forests at low and medium elevations in the Philippines and throughout Southeast Asia. Other genera known for the wholesomeness and palatability of their hearts are *Astrocaryum, Genonoma, Hyospathe, Iriartea, Prestoes, Socrates,* and *Welfia.*

## LIMITATIONS AND SPECIAL REQUIREMENTS

Not all species of palms have edible hearts. Some are bitter or tough, and some may actually be toxic (for example, the heart of *Orania* species). Some hearts are very difficult to remove. Coconut palms are subject to serious diseases (such as lethal yellowing), and it is not known what effect such diseases would have on the quality of the terminal bud at the time of harvest.

## RESEARCH NEEDS

The first requirement is to collect as many promising species as possible in order to select palms appropriate for use as a palm heart plantation crop. Trial plantings should be made to determine if any can surpass the current commercial palm heart sources.

Studies of the botanical, agronomic, and economic aspects of palms as raw material for palm hearts are essential. Surveys should be made of existing palm heart plantations to note the present procedures and possibilities for improvement. Research is needed to clarify the details of productivity, labor requirements, and economic return to grower and processor.

### Selected Readings

Camacho, E., and J. Soria V. 1970. Palmito de pejibaye. *Proceedings Tropical Regional American Society of Horticulture Science.* 14:122-32.
Hodge, W. H. 1965. Palm cabbage. *Principes.* 9(4):124-31.

### Research Contacts and Germ Plasm Sources

Bailey Hortorium, Cornell University, Ithaca, New York 14853, USA (H. E. Moore)
Biological Station, Las Cruces, Costa Rica (R. G. Wilson)
Botanic Gardens, Calcutta, India
Centro de Pesquisas Florestáis, Faculdade de Florestas, Caixa postal 2959, Curitiba, Paraná, Brazil
Centro de Recursos Naturais da Amazônia, Belém, Pará, Brazil
Department of Botany, Smithsonian Institution, Washington, D.C. 20560, USA (R. W. Reed)
Fundação Centro de Desenvolvimento Industrial CEDIN, Rua Álvares Cabral 16, 4° and., Salvador, Bahia, Brazil.
Fundação Coopercotia, Cooperativa Agrícola de Cotia, Cotia, São Paulo, Brazil
Instituto Imteramericano de Ciencias Agrícolas, Turrialba, Costa Rica
Jardín Botánico, Apartado Aéreo 1 5660, Secretaría de Desarrollo y Fomento, Departmento del Valle del Cavea, República de Colombia (V. M. Patiño)
Jardim Botânico, Rio de Janeiro, Brazil (Pe. R. Reitz)
Laboratoire d'Ethnobotanique, Jardin des Plantes, Paris, France (J. Barrau)
Leão, Marilene, and M. Cardoso. 1974. *Instrucões para a Cultura do Palmiteiro (Euterpe edulis).* Superintendencia do Desenvolvimento do Litoral Paulista, Instituto Agronomico de Campinas, São Paulo. Brazil.
Royal Botanic Garden, Peradeniya, Sri Lanka
Summit Gardens, Panama, Panama

# WAX GOURD

Grown throughout the Asian tropics, the wax gourd* is little known elsewhere. Its melon-like fruit has a thick flesh that is white, crisp, and juicy. An outstanding feature is its resistance to spoilage. Preserved from attack of microorganisms by its waxy coating, the fruit can be stored without refrigeration for as long as a year. The plants are prolific, rapid growers (over a 4-day period one shoot grew an average of 2.3 cm every 3 hours[†]). Three or four crops can be produced each year. The wax gourd is now grown mainly as a household crop, but the market could be greatly expanded. It has important potential as a new vegetable for large areas of Latin America and Africa.

The fruit can be consumed during various stages of maturity. The mild-flavored, easily digested flesh may be used as a cucumber substitute, a cooked vegetable, or food extender. The Chinese use it in soup. In India and Cuba, a popular sweet is made by cooking the pulp in syrup.

The fruit contains 96 percent water, 0.4 percent protein, 0.1 percent fat, 3.2 percent carbohydrate, and 0.3 percent mineral matter. There are two distinct types: round and elongated. Hairy when young, they grow to immense proportions. They may measure as much as 2 m long and 1 m in diameter, and weigh up to 35 kg. The thin, tough skin is coated with white, chalky wax. (Some varieties have minute hairs even when mature.) The pulp has many flat, oval, light-brown seeds up to 2.5 cm long, which can be fried and eaten (like pumpkin seeds). They also yield a pale yellow oil, which has not been studied.

Young leaves, flower buds, and vine tips are boiled and eaten as greens.

The plant, an annual, creeping vine, resembles a pumpkin vine. It is reportedly easier to grow than any other cucurbit (pumpkin, squash, melon, etc.). Usually planted on mounds or ridges, the fruit is harvested in less than 5 months; in Sri Lanka, seeds sown in the rainy season produce wax gourds in 2 months. The plants can be grown on a trellis, but since the heavy, succulent fruit needs strong supports, the plants are sometimes grown over roofs and trees. In China the seed is planted on the banks of village ponds, and the plants grow over a bamboo framework erected over water. This method provides abundant water for the plant, and the framework over the water permits the land to be used for other purposes.

---

*Benincasa hispida* (Thumb.) Cogn. (*B. cerifera* Savi.). Also known as white gourd, ash-gourd, and petha. Family: Cucurbitaceae.
[†]Herklots, G. A. C. 1972. See Selected Readings.

Wax gourd.  (J. Morton)

Wax gourd.  (J. Morton)

The wax gourd is relatively drought tolerant. In India, the furrows are flooded at weekly intervals during the dry season, but not during the rainy season unless there has been no precipitation for 10 or 12 days.

The seeds remain viable for 10 years and germinate in 1 or 2 weeks. Pest and disease problems are minimal. Young fruit is protected by its hairy cover, maturing fruit by its waxy coat.

## LIMITATIONS AND SPECIAL REQUIREMENTS

The wax gourd is an ideal food for those with excess weight or digestive problems. Its only handicap is its mild taste. Those accustomed to richer fare may not like it without the addition of seasonings or other vegetables or fruits of strong flavor. It is similar in flavor and texture to the chayote (*Sechium edule*).

Wax gourds grow best in medium-dry lowlands. They do not grow well in high-rainfall areas.

## RESEARCH NEEDS

Minimal research is needed to extend the use of wax gourds. The primary need is to acquaint farmers and consumers with its possibilities.

Food technology studies to develop its market potential could help its introduction to new areas.

Commercial seed sources are needed.

### Selected Readings

Agnibotri, B. N. 1948. Petha—its cultivation and economic uses. I & II *Indian Food Packer*. 2(2):9-10; and 2(12):17-18.

Herklots, G. A. C. 1972. *Vegetables in South-East Asia*. Hafner Press, Macmillan Publishing Co., Inc., New York.

Morton, J. F. 1971. The wax gourd—a year-round Florida vegetable with unusual keeping quality. *Proceedings of Florida State Horticulture Society*. 84:104-9.

Srivastava, V. K., and S. C. P. Sachan. 1969. Grow ash-gourd the efficient way. *Indian Horticulture*. 14(1):13-5.

### Research Contacts and Germ Plasm Supply

Department of Horticulture, Chia-yi Agriculture Experiment Station, Chia-yi, Taiwan, China (Chu Ching-Kuo, Head)

Hawaii Agricultural Experiment Station, Honolulu, Hawaii 96822, USA (S. Nakahara)

Tropi-Pak, 3664 N.W. 48th St., Miami, Florida 33142, USA (D. Murasaki)

E. R. Witt, 1037 Brock St., Corpus Christi, Texas 78412, USA

# WINGED BEAN

The winged bean*† is a tropical legume with a multitude of exceptionally large nitrogen-fixing nodules. It produces seeds, pods, and leaves (all edible by humans or livestock) with unusually high protein levels; tuberous roots with exceptional amounts of protein; and an edible seed oil.

The winged bean has important potential for small-scale farmers. It is a fast-growing perennial that is particularly valuable because it grows in the wet tropics where protein deficiency in human diets is not only great but difficult to remedy. Winged bean seeds rival soybeans in oil and protein content, and the plant has the added advantages of protein-rich roots and edible foliage.

Though relatively unknown, this multipurpose legume appears to meet many dietary needs of the tropics. It is grown in quantity only in Papua New Guinea and Southeast Asia.

A twining vine, it grows to over 3 m when supported. The pods have four longitudinal jagged "wings" and they contain up to 20 seeds, each weighing about 3 gm. The smooth, shiny seeds may be white, brown, black or mottled. The roots are numerous: they grow horizontally at shallow depth and become thick and tuberous about 2 months after planting. Excellent nodulation without need for inoculation has occurred wherever the crop is grown, even on sites cleared from virgin forest. Individual winged bean plants may carry over 600 nodules, and the fresh weight of the large nodules can reach 0.85 tons/ha.‡

Neither pests nor disease appear to be a serious threat. Nor do soil requirements appear to be demanding. Winged bean crops have always been grown in regions having fairly heavy rainfall. The lower limit has not been established. The plant thrives in regions with an annual rainfall of 250 cm or more.

The winged bean is cultivated largely for its young, tender pods, which are sliced and cooked, much like green beans. Pods are picked beginning 10 weeks after sowing, and the plant continues to bear pods indefinitely. The young leaves and shoots may also be eaten as a leafy vegetable.

Unripe seeds can be used in soups. Ripe seeds are roasted and eaten like peanuts. The nutritive value of the ripe, dry seeds is very close to that of

---

*Psophocarpus tetragonolobus* (L.) DC. Also known as four-angled bean, Goa bean, asparagus pea. Family: Leguminosae.

†The exceptional promise of this plant is detailed in a companion publication, *The Winged Bean: A High Protein Crop for the Tropics*, available without charge. To order see page 188.

‡Masefield. 1961. See Selected Readings.

In Papua New Guinea winged beans are grown on stakes for pods and seeds (background) and grown unstaked for tubers and as a ground cover (foreground). The plant grows vigorously, forming dense masses of vegetation. Prostrate plants seldom flower, but staked plants flower and bear copious fruit. (N. D. Vietmeyer)

soybeans (34 percent protein and 18 percent oil*). The protein is high in lysine—8 percent of the total amino-acid content (without tryptophan). More than 60 percent of the fatty acids in the oil are unsaturated. The seeds are rich in tocopherol, an antioxidant that increases vitamin A use in the human body (vitamin A deficiency is common in many tropical regions).

The winged bean may have high yield potential. Yields of about 2.5 tons of seed/ha have been reported.† If this is confirmed as a fair average the winged bean will be among the top-yielding tropical grain legumes.

The immature tuberous roots are eaten like potatoes. They are reported to contain over 20 percent protein (dry weight basis). An edible tropical root crop with such high protein content could be of immense help in reducing protein malnutrition, particularly since winged beans grow well in the regions where inhabitants already live on low protein root crops such as cassava.

Perhaps after harvesting the crop for pods, seeds, or roots, the haulm can be fed to animals. It is reportedly palatable to livestock.‡ Like all other parts of the winged bean, the foliage has a remarkably high protein content.

## LIMITATIONS AND SPECIAL REQUIREMENTS

Winged bean varieties now cultivated for pods and seeds must be grown on stakes. This—and the fact that all pods do not ripen simultaneously—restricts

*Pospisil *et al* 1971. See Selected Readings.
†*Ibid.*
‡*Ibid.*

Small charcoal-blackened winged bean tubers cooked in hot ashes by highland tribesmen in Papua New Guinea. The tubers contain ten or twenty times the protein of other root crops. (N. D. Vietmeyer)

their use to the small (or village) farmer. The winged bean cannot yet be considered for mass commercial planting.

Because of antinutrition factors, mature winged bean seeds must first be cooked before they can be used for human consumption.* This phenomenon is common to several other leguminous seeds, including soybeans. Immature seeds can be eaten raw without ill effects.

The climatic requirements of the winged bean have not been studied in depth.

## RESEARCH NEEDS

A detailed analysis of winged bean research needs appears in the companion report: *The Winged Bean: A High-Protein Crop for the Tropics.* (See page 187.

Because seed sources are scarce, the varietal composition is virtually unknown. It will be necessary to collect several varieties, especially in Southeast Asia; to propagate them; and to run comparative trials (with seed from various sources) in the wet tropics of Africa, Latin America, and Asia.

The chief obstacle to the further investigation of the crop is the difficulty in obtaining seed. There is little available because there has never been a need for it in quantity. Seed supplies must be increased before large-scale experiments can be undertaken. The best seed available must be used; a random selection may lead to unjustifiably poor results.

Variations in pod length and number of seeds per pod should be considered when seeking high-yielding varieties. There may also be genetic variation in root yield, or in foliage yield and composition. Only comparative trials can provide definitive answers.

The phenology of different varieties should be studied for use in breeding programs aimed at producing high-yielding types with uniform time of flowering and seed maturation.

Research is needed to find agronomic practices, climatic conditions, and soil conditions that give optimum yields.

The relative yield of pods and seeds from supported and unsupported plants should be explored. It would be useful to investigate the possibility of harvesting first a seed crop and then a root crop, maintaining reasonable yields for both.

The winged bean's ability to enhance soil fertility for subsequent crops is worth detailed examination. It would also be beneficial to determine its use as a forage.

*Crevost and Lemarié. 1921. See Selected Readings.

Possible toxicants and antinutrition factors in the mature seeds need analysis and detailed study. Research should also include an amino acid assay and an investigation into the overall nutritional value of the roots.

Other major research needs include:

• Determining digestibility of protein at different stages of development of leaves, stems, pods, etc.;

• Investigating seed physiology and the germination and storage of seeds;

• Developing ways to prepare the dry beans and roots; and

• Studying the plant's palatability and value for livestock.

## Selected Readings

Burkhill, I. H. 1935. *Dictionary of the Economic Products of the Malay Peninsula*. Vol. 2. Greenwood Press, Inc., Westport, Connecticut, USA.

Crévost, C., and C. Lemarié. 1921. Catalogue des produits de l'Indochine. *Bulletin Economique de l'Indochine*. 23:121.

Masefield, G. B. 1967. The intensive production of grain legumes in the tropics. *Soil and Crop Science Society of Florida Proceedings*. 27:338.

Masefield, G. B. 1961. Root nodulation and agricultural potential of the leguminous genus Psophocarpus. *Tropical Agriculture, Trinidad*. 38:225.

Masefield, G. B. 1973. *Psophocarpus tetragonolobus*—a crop with a future? *Field Crop Abstracts*. 26(4):157-160.

Winged beans are commonly seen in vegetable markets in Thailand. They are widely used in soups, chow mein, and other traditional dishes. (N. D. Vietmeyer)

National Academy of Sciences. 1975. *The Winged Bean: A High-Protein Crop for the Tropics.* Washington, D.C., USA.

Pospisil, F., S. K. Karikari, and E. Boamah-Mensah. 1971. Investigations of winged bean in Ghana. *World Crops.* 23:260-4.

Purseglove, J. W. 1968. *Tropical Crops: Dicotyledons.* Vol. 1. John Wiley, New York.

## Research Contacts and Germ Plasm Supply

Agricultural Research Station, University of Ghana, Kade, Ghana (S. K. Karakari).

Department of Agriculture, University of Papua and New Guinea, P. O. University, Papua New Guinea (T. N. Khan).

Department of Agricultural Science, University of Oxford, United Kingdom (G. B. Masefield)

Department of Agronomy, University of Illinois, Urbana, Illinois 61801, USA (T. Hymowitz).

International Institute of Tropical Agriculture, P.M.B. 5320, Ibadan, Nigeria (K. O. Rachie).

A more complete list of research contacts can be found in the National Academy of Sciences' report noted above.

# IV FRUITS

## DURIAN

Although the durian* is grown only in Malaysia, Indonesia, southern Thailand, and the Philippines, it is one of the best known and most controversial of all fruits. Though there are many places in the West Indies, tropical America, Africa, and Oceania where it should grow well, the durian is important only to Southeast Asia. It has received no research attention and today our knowledge of durian is virtually the same as when, in the 15th century, it was first observed by Europeans.

Though Malays and other people in the Far East are very partial to it, the fruit has met with a mixed reception from Europeans. Many are repelled by its strong, disagreeable odor, but others quickly become extremely fond of it. The taste, difficult to describe, is sweet, aromatic, and persistent. The odor has been referred to as "a mixture of old cheese and onions flavored with turpentine" or as "custard passed through a sewer." But durian enthusiasts are not bothered by the odor: the 19th-century British naturalist, Alfred Russel Wallace, considered that "it was worth a journey to the East, if only to taste of its fruit."†

The huge fruit vary from spherical to oval and may grow as large as 30 cm long and 15 cm in diameter and weigh up to 20 kg each. Their hard, thick skins are covered with sharp prickles. The interior is divided into five cells, each containing up to four seeds enveloped in a firm, cream-colored pulp. Nutritionally, the fruit is an important source of carbohydrate, fat, and vitamins, and contains some protein.

Durian can be prepared in various ways. The ripe pulp is commonly eaten fresh, or it can be preserved for use in ice cream, candy, or other sweets. The

*Durio zibethinus* Murr. and related species. Family: Bombacaceae.
†He also described it as "a rich butter-like custard highly flavoured with almonds, but intermingled with it come wafts of flavour that call to mind cream-cheese, onion sauce, brown-sherry, and other incongruities. Then there is a rich glutinous smoothness in the pulp which nothing else possesses, but which adds to its delicacy. It is neither acid nor sweet, nor juicy, yet one feels the want of none of these qualities for it is perfect as it is."

pulp of unripe fruit may be used as a vegetable. When cooked the seed is also edible.

Wild animals, particularly elephants, tigers, and monkeys, are very attracted to the fruit. Harvesters build shelters beneath wild durian trees so they can get to the fruit before the animals.

There are at least five species of durian, but only one is well known. The others, all potentially important species, are virtually unknown, even in Malaysia. Several have edible fruits said to taste as good as (or better than) the common durian. The species are:

• *Durio zibethinus* Murrs. (the common durian) Distribution: widespread throughout Southeast Asia. Haphazardly cultivated or semiwild.

• *Durio kutejensis* Becc. Distribution: Borneo (Kalimantan, Sarawak, and Sabah). Slightly cultivated, but mainly wild.

• *Durio oxleyanus* Griff. Distribution: South Sumatra and Borneo. Little known even locally; exclusively a wild plant.

• *Durio graveolens* Becc. Distribution: East Borneo. Rare wild and even rarer cultivated.

• *Durio dulcis* Becc. Distribution: Borneo. Only in the wild.

Odor varies greatly among the five species. Some have only a slight odor; *Durio graveolens* produces odorless fruit. One variety of *Durio kutejensis* has a mild, inoffensive odor.

*Durio kutejensis* may offer better fruit quality than the common durian because its flexible soft spines make it easier to handle.

All five species are medium-sized or large trees, 20-40 m tall. Usually propagated from seeds, they grow vigorously. They are planted in humid lowland areas below 800 m elevation. Improved varieties can be easily reproduced by budding them onto 1-year-old rootstocks of the same species.

Durian trees are productive and, even with little care, provide important revenue for villagers and farmers.


## LIMITATIONS AND SPECIAL REQUIREMENTS

As mentioned, the strong odor is offensive to many people. It is attributed to indole derivatives.

There has been little attempt to organize durian marketing, quality control, harvesting, etc.

The trees are slow to produce and only begin bearing after 7 years. Each fruit takes 3 months to develop and is not fully ripe until it drops from the tree. Falling fruit is a hazard for gatherers.

Durian fruits. (E. S. Ayensu)

The custard-like pulp must be eaten shortly after harvest because it quickly turns rancid and sour. Since fruit is not easily transported, only local distribution of fresh fruit can be considered at present.

The seeds quickly lose their viability, which makes it difficult to introduce the species to other regions. A few durian trees have been introduced to Honduras, however, and the fruits are much sought after (apparently the odor was not an insurmountable obstacle).

Since durian trees in Southeast Asia neither receive nor require much attention nothing is known about the best methods for pruning, irrigation, pest control, etc.

The tree does not thrive where there is a distinct dry season.


## RESEARCH NEEDS

Durian horticulture, breeding, and selection are needed. Durians have many varieties that offer great possibilities for improvement, but detailed analysis is still lacking. Agronomic research is needed to select elite strains from each species, improve horticultural practices, and introduce durians to new tropical regions.

Food technology research is needed, particularly for preserving, transporting, and processing the fruit or flesh.

### Selected Readings

Ochse, J. J. et al. 1961. *Tropical and Subtropical Agriculture*. The Macmillan Company, Collier-Macmillan Ltd., London.

Popenoe, W. 1920. *Manual of Tropical and Subtropical Fruits*. The Macmillan Company, New York.

Soegeng Reksodihardjo, W. 1962. The species of *Durio* with edible fruits. *Economic Botany*. 16(4):270-82.

Stanton, W. R. 1966. The chemical composition of some tropical food plants: VI. Durian. *Tropical Science*. 8(1):6-10.

Valmayor, R. V., R. E. Coronel, and D. A. Ramírez. 1965. Studies on floral biology, fruit set and fruit development in durian. *Philippines Agriculture*. 48(8-9):355-66.

Wyatt-Smith, J. 1953. Materials for a revision of Malayan *Durio* with notes on Bornean species. *Kew Bulletin*. 4:513-34.

### Research Contacts and Germ Plasm Supply

Herbarium Bogoriense, Bogor, Indonesia. (A. Kostermans)

W. Soegeng Reksodihardjo, Pioneer Hi-Bred International Inc., Des Moines, Iowa 50309, USA.

University Herbarium, School of Biological Sciences, University of Malaya, Kuala Lumpur, Malaysia (B. C. Stone)

# MANGOSTEEN

Often described as one of the world's best-flavored fruit, the mangosteen* is highly esteemed in Southeast Asia. In other tropical areas this fruit is known only in botanical gardens and small experimental orchards. Curiously, it is unavailable in what could be its major markets: Central America, South America, Australia, and Africa, where it would be readily accepted if it could be economically produced. It also has great potential for export to North America, Europe, and the Middle East.

Mangosteen culture has been attempted in many humid, lowland tropical areas. However, because of horticultural difficulties no widespread commercial production has been successful—even in the Far East where the fruit, which commands high prices, is picked from uncultivated, wild trees. Extending its use offers a formidable research challenge.

The mangosteen grows in high rainfall areas—over 2,500 mm per year—where, because of the high humidity, few commercial crops can be economically cultivated.

The fruit—the size of a tennis ball—contains a segmented, white (almost translucent) pulp that is protected by a purple shell 6 mm thick. The pulp is sweet, subacid, and agreeably flavored. Of all the exotic tropical fruits the mangosteen is perhaps the one most readily accepted by western palates.

The tree is a slow-growing evergreen with large, dark green leaves. It thrives best in warm, humid, rainy climates with few seasonal variations in rainfall and temperature. But mangosteen trees have been grown successfully under dry conditions with irrigation. Temperatures between 20° and 30°C are ideal, especially if they are not subject to sudden changes—cool spells (4°C) can be fatal to young trees. The trees rarely grow over 10 m in height.

Deep, fertile, well-drained, slightly acid soils are needed to grow the best trees and to produce the heaviest yields. Under such conditions, yields of 200-800 fruits per tree have been obtained in good years. They are harvested at maturity and must be handled carefully to prevent damage. The tough, thick rinds should enable the fruit to be shipped and marketed. If refrigerated, the fruit can be stored for several weeks.

## LIMITATIONS AND SPECIAL REQUIREMENTS

Though the mangosteen has long been regarded as having great potential if its horticultural limitations could be eliminated, it has received very little research attention from trained horticulturists. Consequently, today there are

*Garcinia mangostana L. Family: Guttiferae.

Mangosteen fruit. (U. S. Department of Agriculture)

no improved varieties that sustain high production and that have good commercial characteristics. The horticultural limitations are due to the following factors:

• Mangosteen seeds reproduce the characters only of the mother plant; there is no genetic variation produced. This makes the production of superior types difficult.

• Growers hesitate to plant mangosteen orchards because of the delay before their investment brings return: seedlings take as long as 15 years to produce a profitable crop.

• No reliable method has been found for propagating the plants vegetatively.

• It is difficult to establish the plant in environments other than those identical to its natural habitat.

• Mangosteen plants tend to bear only in alternate years.

## RESEARCH NEEDS

To stimulate mangosteen production and make it commercially viable, considerable research should be directed toward solving its basic horticultural problems.

Research is needed to discover ways of shortening the time the plants take to mature. There is particular need to develop better vegetative propagation methods (for example, to find rootstocks suitable for grafting). Mangosteen appears to be graft-compatable with other species of *Garcinia.*

## Selected Readings

Hume, E. P. 1950. Difficulties in mangosteen culture. *Malayan Agriculture Journal.* 33(2):104-7.

Krishnamurthi, S., and V. N. Madhava Rao. 1965. The mangosteen, its introduction and establishment in peninsular India. In *Advances in Agricultural Science.* pp. 401-20. Agricultural College and Research Institute, Coimbatore, India.

Ochse, J. J. *et al.* 1961. *Tropical and Subtropical Agriculture.* The Macmillan Company, Collier-Macmillan Ltd., London, England.

Popenoe, W. 1920. *Manual of Tropical and Subtropical Fruits.* The Macmillan Company, New York.

Pynaert, E. 1954. *Le mangoustanier.* Tract no 37. Publication de la Direction de l'Agriculture des Foret et de l'Elevage, Brussels, Belgium.

## Research Contacts and Germ Plasm

Agricultural College and Research Institute, Coimbatore, India (S. Krishnamurthi)
Botanic Gardens, Kebun Raya, Bogor, Indonesia (S. Idris)
Department of Agriculture, Bangkok, Thailand (Pairoj Pholprasit)

# NARANJILLA

Naranjilla,* "the golden fruit of the Andes," has great potential for the future, though at present it is little known outside its native home, Colombia and Ecuador. An excellent dessert fruit, it is also used to flavor confections, jelly, jam, and other preserves.

Freshly squeezed naranjilla juice is used in Ecuador and Colombia to make *sorbete*, a green, foamy drink with an appealing sweet-sour flavor of pineapple and strawberry. In Panama, Guatemala, and Costa Rica, where the plant has been introduced, the fresh juice is processed into frozen concentrate.

The plant is a large, robust shrub (1-2 m high) with hairy leaves and spherical yellow-orange fruit, sometimes as large as tennis balls, densely covered with easily removed white hairs. The acidulous, yellow-green pulp has numerous seeds. Unaffected by season, fruit is produced throughout the year.

*Solanum quitoense* Lam. Also known as lulo. Family: Solanaceae.

The shrubby naranjilla bush under cultivation in Ecuador. (C. B. Heiser)

Naranjilla fruit.  (W. H. Hodge)

In Ecuador, the naranjilla grows best on fertile, well-drained slopes of humid, upland valleys where the annual rainfall is at least 1,500 mm. The plant grows rapidly and bears large quantities of fruit. It yields 1,000 to 2,000 kg of fruit per ha with little care.

## LIMITATIONS AND SPECIAL REQUIREMENTS

The plants have exacting climatic requirements. Frost sensitive, they need good drainage and moderately cool and rather humid climate at altitudes of 800-2,000 m. The plant does not thrive in the lowlands.

They are susceptible to rootknot nematodes, viruses, fungal disease, and parasites, which shorten life and reduce production, particularly in sandy soils. Therefore, in Ecuador, new land—uncontaminated by these pests—is used for each planting. Seedlings or grafted plants begin to bear when they are 6-12 months old and continue to produce fruit for about 2 years before they begin to lose vigor (because of the pests) and must be replaced.

The naranjilla plant is easily controllable in Colombia and Ecuador. However, it is a well-established weed in some localities of Costa Rica.

The plants need frequent fertilization (preferably once a month) and water during dry periods.

*Solanum quitoense* in the public market, Pasto, Colombia. (R. E. Schultes)

## RESEARCH NEEDS

Little improvement of naranjilla has been attempted. Research emphasis should be on finding varieties and rootstocks resistant to nematodes and the fungal and bacterial diseases that limit production. The closely related *Solanum hirtum* crosses with naranjilla, is tolerant of rootknot nematodes, and is a promising species for breeding and rootstock. Another nematode-resistant relative is *Solanum macranthum*. It may make good rootstock.

Widening naranjilla's adaptation to climate and soil type would increase its use throughout the tropics. Research is therefore recommended. Investigators should test *Solanum topiro*, crossed or grafted with naranjilla, because it grows at lower elevations and yields a larger (also popular) fruit.

### Selected Readings

García-Reyes, F. 1967. El cultivo de lulo en la zona cafetera colombiana. *Revista Cafetera.* 17(142):75-7.

Gattoni, L. A. 1961. *La naranjilla.* Ministerio de Agricultura, Panama.

Heiser, C. B., Jr. 1969. *Nightshades, the Paradoxical Plants.* W. H. Freeman and Co., San Francisco.

Hodge, W. H. 1947. El lulo, una fruta andina poco conocida. *Revista Facultad Nacional de Agronomía,* Medellím, Colombia 7:147.

Hodge, W. H. 1947. Naranjillas, or "little oranges" of the Andean Highlands. *Journal New York Botanical Gardens.* 48(571):155-60.

Ledin, R. B. 1952. The naranjilla (*Solanum quitoense* Lam.). *Proceedings of Florida State Horticulture Society.* 65:187-90.

Munier, R. 1962. La culture du lulo en Colombia. *Fruits.* 17(2):91-3.

Pacheco, R., and J. Jiménez. 1968. *El cultivo de la naranjilla en el Ecuador.* Ministerio de Agricultura y Ganaderia, Quito, Ecuador.

Patiño, V. M. 1963. *Plantas cultivadas y animales domésticos en America equinoccial.* V. 1. Printing Department, Cali, Colombia. p. 403.

Schultes, R. E., and J. Cuatrecasas. 1953. Notes on the cultivated lulo. *Harvard University Botanical Museum Leaflets.* 16:97.

Schultes, R. E. and R. Romero-Castañeda. 1962. Edible fruits of Solanum in Colombia. *Harvard University Botanical Museum Leaflets.* 19:235-286.

Romero-Castañeda, R. 1961. El lulo: una fruta de importancia económica. *Agricultura Tropical.* 17(4):214-18.

### Research Contacts and Germ Plasm Supply

Agriculture Attaché, American Embassy, San Jose, Costa Rica (A. G. Krevorkian)

CATIE, Inter American Institute of Agricultural Sciences, Turrialba, Costa Rica (J. Soria V.)

Indiana University, Bloomington, Indiana 61701, USA (C. B. Heiser)

Jardín Botánico, Universidad del Valle, Cali, Colombia (V. M. Patiño)

Jefe Seccion de Botánica, Instituto de Ciencias Naturales, Apartado 7495, Bogotá, Colombia

# PEJIBAYE

Other than the coconut, date, and African oil palm, few plants of the family Palmae have been widely exploited. Many could become useful sources of oil and food. A notable example is pejibaye, or peach palm.* It could become an important commercial crop throughout the humid tropics. Probably the most balanced of all tropical foods, its fruit contains carbohydrates, protein, oil, minerals, and vitamins.

Although favorably mentioned by Spanish writers centuries ago, pejibaye today is little known outside Central America and northern South America. It is a palm with many spiny trunks emerging from a common root stock. The fruit, 2-6 cm long, is borne in bunches weighing up to 12.5 kg and consisting of up to 300 fruits. There may be as much as 13 bunches on a single trunk and, under ideal conditions, two crops are harvested per year. The fruit is a starchy mesocarp surrounding a seed. It is not sweet; its flavor and texture are reminiscent of chestnuts. Pejibaye fruit has twice the protein content of banana and can provide more carbohydrate and protein per hectare than maize.

Pejibaye fruit is usually prepared by boiling in salted water. The skin is removed before eating. To preserve the fruit, it is boiled and then dried. It can be restored to original consistency and flavor—even after 6 months or more—by a second brief boiling. It is also delicious when roasted.

In addition to the fleshy mesocarp, the white, hard-shelled seed kernel is sometimes eaten. It tastes somewhat like coconut and has a high percentage of oil.

Planted in tropical America since ancient times, sizable pejibaye stands now exist in Costa Rica, and innumerable dooryard trees are scattered over the lowlands of Brazil, Costa Rica, Panama, Colombia, Peru, Venezuela, and Ecuador. The pejibaye is of major economic importance throughout the region. At least part of the year it supplies the principal food for many inhabitants.

The plant is adapted to tropical conditions, preferring regions where annual rainfall is 2,500 mm or less. In Costa Rica it grows at all elevations from sea level to 1,200 m, and occasionally as high as 1,500 m. It grows best in heavy soil: clay loam, or clay.

---

*Guilielma gasipaes (H.B.K.) L. H. Bailey. Formerly known as Guilielma speciosa Mart. and Guilielma utilis Oerst. Also known as Bactris gasipaes H.B.K. and Guilielma chontaduro Triana. Commonly called pejibay (Central America) also spelled pejivalle, etc., piriguao (Venezuela), pijuajo (Peru), paripou (French Guiana), and pupunha (Brazil). Family: Palmae

Pejibaye fruits. (P. H. Allen, courtesy W. H. Hodge)

Commonly, propagation is by seeds, although the plants form suckers readily (an important benefit for commercial plantings for it allows superior varieties to be replicated easily). When grown from seed, the pejibaye begins to bear after 6 or 8 years and has an economic life of 75 years or more. Once established, the plant requires little care.

Varieties of the pejibaye are not well defined, but there are many. Varietal differences in fruit size, fruit-cluster size, spine length, and fruit color are known.

Because of its multiple stems pejibaye is one of the most promising palms for the plantation production of hearts of palm (see page 49).

Pejibaye. (W. H. Hodge)

## LIMITATIONS AND SPECIAL REQUIREMENTS

The major barrier to propagating large numbers of pejibaye for commercial plantations is the lack of superior cultivars. There is a scarcity of elite stock material (suckers). Seedlings vary too much in quality and performance—and take too long to bear—to warrant large investment. Existing selections are not sufficiently productive, despite claims to the contrary. Seedless (parthenocarpic) types are lower in quality and color and are not so productive as seeded types.

The trunks of most pejibaye strains are densely covered with spines, but the northwest Amazon has spineless races. Harvesting is difficult and expensive. Cutting off too many of the spines kills the palm.

## RESEARCH NEEDS

Collection of seed, classification of cultivars, diffusion of seed, and information on the pejibaye crop could lead to its cultivation in many areas. An intensive campaign is necessary to expand its cultivation, beginning with the areas in which it is already familiar.

Efforts must be concentrated on management and varietal selection (especially to select spineless varieties). There are some little-known varieties, mostly found in the northwest Amazon region, that lack spines. These should be collected and selected for use in propagation and crossbreeding.

Food technologists should test ways to can and preserve pejibaye because at present the fruit is not easy to store or transport in quantity. So far, most food research has concentrated on its nutritive value.

Agronomists should study the value of interplanting other crops among the pejibaye for this could provide a cash return while the pejibaye are maturing.

The pejibaye research at Centro Agronómico Tropical de Investigación y Enseñanza in Turrialba, Costa Rica, should receive full support from technical assistance agencies. Funds should also be allocated for a campaign to extend their results to other tropical countries.

### Selected Readings

Johannessen, C. L. 1966. Pejibaye palm: yields, prices and labor costs. *Economic Botany*. 20(3):302-15.

Johannessen, C. L. 1966. Pejibayes in commercial production. *Turrialba*. 16(2):181-7. (Available from the author, address below.)

Johannessen, C. L. 1967. Pejibaye palm: physical and chemical analysis of the fruit. *Economic Botany*. 21(4):371-8.

Patiño, V. M. 1958. El cachipay o pijibay, en la cultura de los indígenas de la America intertropical. Instituto Indigenista Interamericano. Mexico. Ediciones Especiales. 39:176-203, 293-331.

Popenoe, W. and O. Jiménez. 1921. The pejibaye, a neglected food plant of tropical America. *Journal of Heredity*. 12(4):151-66.

Seibert, R. J. 1950. The importance of palms to Latin America; pejibaye a notable example. *Ceiba*. 1(2):65-74.

### Research Contacts and Germ Plasm Supply

Centro Agrónomico Tropical de Investigación y Enseñanza, Turrialba, Costa Rica (E. Camacho)

Centro Regional de Investigaciones Agropecuarias del Noroeste, Ministerio de Agricultúra, Tarapoto, Perú (M. Slaveria)

Department of Geography, University of Oregon, Eugene, Oregon 97403, USA (C. L. Johannessen)

Instituto de Investigaciones Agro Industriales, Lima, Perú (C. Florez Cossio)

# PUMMELO

To produce fruit of high quality and maximum yield most citrus crops (i.e., oranges, lemons, tangerines, tangelos) require subtropical climates with cool winters and warm summers. The pummelo,* however, is a citrus fruit ideally suited to the vast lowland tropical zone; the uniformly warm climate reduces the quality and yield of other citrus, but the pummelo appears to thrive.

The pummelo is native to Southeast Asia where it has been cultivated for centuries. In Thailand, where it is most highly cultivated, fine commercial varieties—with a shelf life as long as 4 months—have been exported to neighboring countries for more than 60 years.

An attribute of the pummelo is its relatively high tolerance to saline conditions. This tolerance has been exploited in Thailand; unproductive coastal lowlands around river deltas and brackish marshy areas are devoted to pummelo cultivation. The popular belief in Thailand is that the flavor and quality of the fruit are enhanced by the salt. However, this is questionable and requires experimental proof.

Pummelo is a crop with potential for coastal lowlands elsewhere in the

---

*Citrus grandis* (L.) Osbeck. Also known as shaddock, toronja, pamplemousse, etc. Family: Rutaceae.

Pummelo. (K. and J. Morton)

Pummelo tree, Florida. (J. Morton)

tropics, especially those where climate, moisture, and salinity prevent cultivation of other popular citrus fruits.

Although the pummelo has been introduced into citrus-growing areas of the world, the varieties chosen produced disappointing fruit, inferior in quality to the best in Southeast Asia.

Pummelo trees are generally medium sized, 5-15 m tall when mature. They have broad, shiny leaves; the young branches are covered with spines. The fruit is green or yellow and is the largest among the citrus varieties, larger even than grapefruit. They are either spherical or pear shaped, and have a thick (up to 2 cm) rind. The internal segments are formed of firm juice sacs (vesicles). The best varieties have a pleasant balance of acid and sugar and leave no bitter aftertaste.

## LIMITATIONS AND SPECIAL REQUIREMENTS

For optimum performance, pummelos require warm, frost-free climates with well-drained soils and adequate moisture.

There are few research or agricultural extension reports on pummelos.

Citrus canker is a common affliction of pummelo trees in Southeast Asia.

## RESEARCH NEEDS

Considerable information on pummelos has been accumulated by generations of growers in Southeast Asia. It needs to be collated and evaluated by experienced horticulturists. But more data are needed if pummelo cultivation is to be adapted successfully outside Southeast Asia. We must know about varietal behavior, such as the best rootstocks for different soils, the unpredictable seedlessness of some types, and the tolerance and susceptibility to diseases.

Research to select superior varieties is helped by the genetic characteristics of pummelo: the seeds of most citrus tend to reproduce the characters of the mother plant, but pummelo seeds are gametic (they contain only one embryo, which is subject to genetic segregation) and give rise to plants with entirely new horticultural characters. This produces a wealth of varieties to choose from.

Testing of rootstocks and cultivars in different kinds of soils is also needed, especially in coastal, saline-soil locations.

Using superior varieties collected in Southeast Asia, scientists should establish test plots in new tropical locales in Africa, Latin America, Oceania, and Australia.

## Selected Readings

Fairchild, D. 1927. The pink fleshed pummelo of Java. *Journal of Heredity*. 18(10):425-7.

Groff, G. W. 1927. Culture and varieties of the Siamese pummelo as related to introductions into other countries. *Linnean Society Journal*. 5(3):187-254.

Ochse, J. J., M. H. Soule, Jr., M. J. Dijkman, and C. Wehlburg. 1961. *Tropical and Subtropical Agriculture, Vol. 1*. Collier-Macmillan, Ltd., London.

Reuther, W., *et al.* 1967. *The Citrus Industry*. Vol. 1. University of California at Riverside, Riverside, California.

Soost, R. K. 1964. Self-incompatibility in *Citrus grandis* (L.). *Proceedings of the American Horticulture Society*. 84:137-40.

## Research Contacts and Germ Plasm Supply

Agricultural Research and Educational Center, University of Florida, 18905 S.W. 280th Street, Homestead, Florida 33030, USA (S. Malo)

Department of Agriculture, Bangkok, Thailand (Pairoj Pholprasit)

University of California at Riverside, Riverside, California 92502, USA (R. K. Soost)

# SOURSOP

The soursop* is a tropical fruit with potential for development as a processed industrial commodity. Native to and common in tropical America and the West Indies, it was one of the first fruits carried from the New World to other tropical regions. It has become popular in areas as diverse as southern China, Australia, and Africa. Though mainly eaten as a fresh fruit, soursop can be processed and preserved without losing its aromatic flavor. Because of its distinctive qualities and its desirability for puree, nectar, ice cream, and jelly, it offers developing countries excellent export possibilities. European and North American markets appear particularly promising.

The soursop tree flowers and bears fruit more or less continuously, though there usually is a principal ripening season. Varying in form and size, the fruit often weighs 4 kg or more. The white, fibrous, juicy flesh smells somewhat like pineapple, but the musky, rather acid flavor is unique. Soursops are usually cut in sections and the flesh eaten with a spoon. The pulp is often added to fruit cups or salads, or chilled and served as dessert, but generally it

---

*Annona muricata* L. Also known as guanábana (in Spanish) and graviola (in Brazil). Family: Annonaceae.

is used in ice cream or is mixed with water and sugar to make a refreshing drink. Frozen pulp is sold in plastic bags in Philippine supermarkets; fresh juice is marketed in waxed, cardboard cartons in the Netherlands Antilles.

The soursop fruit has many black seeds scattered through the pulp, but most of its closely packed segments are seedless. The fruit contains 12 percent sugar, mostly glucose, and some fructose and pectin that in commercial operations could be an important by-product.

The tree, low-branching and bushy—but slender because of its upturned limbs—reaches a maximum height of 8-10 m. Seldom grown in commercial orchards, it is often planted in backyard gardens. The tree is easily propagated by budding onto rootstocks of the same species. Seedlings or grafted plants grow rapidly and bear fruit by the third year.

## LIMITATIONS AND SPECIAL REQUIREMENTS

Adapted only to lowland areas, the soursop is widely planted in the tropics below an altitude of 1,000 m. It requires an annual rainfall of 100 cm or more. It will not tolerate dry, cold winds and, least hardy of the annonas, it produces few fruits in chilly, mountainous areas. Though it will not tolerate waterlogging, the soursop can be grown in a wide variety of soils.

Soursop fruit. (K. and J. Morton)

Soursop tree, Florida.  (J. Morton)

Soursops are soft and perishable when ripe, and they ferment quickly. Consequently, they are difficult to transport and are not exported as fresh fruits.

The tree, unfortunately, is not prolific, the usual crop being only 12-24 fruits per tree. In Puerto Rico, production of 2½-4 tons of fruit per acre is considered a good yield from well-tended trees. Generous fertilization will increase the crop.

The flowers are pollinated by insects, usually beetles. Pollination by hand encourages fruit-set because pollen is often shed before the stigma is receptive, and small, malformed fruits result.

In very humid areas of El Salvador it has been observed that soursop trees often grow well, but bear only a few poor-quality fruits. Most of their flowers and young fruit fall due to anthracnose caused by the fungus *Colletotrichum gloeosporioides* Penz. Anthracnose can be controlled with fungicides. Mealy bugs, fruit flies, and red spiders are common pests, but can be controlled with appropriate pesticides. In Surinam and Trinidad, fruit must be bagged to avoid stunting and malformation caused by the soursop moth and soursop wasp, which infest young fruit and seeds.

Soursop seeds are toxic, and care must be taken to assure that all are removed before the pulp is processed.


## RESEARCH NEEDS

The main research needs of soursop are agronomic. Agronomists should investigate pollination and fruit-set problems thoroughly so that fruit production can be improved.

A search should be made for prolific cultivars (with good horticultural characteristics) that produce good-sized, low-fiber fruit with superior keeping quality. Exceptionally large and well-formed soursops have been seen on the market in Buga, Colombia, and Saigon, South Vietnam.


### Selected Readings

Benero, J. R., A. J. Rodríguez, and A. Roman de Sandoval. 1971. A soursop pulp extraction procedure. *Journal of Agriculture*. University of Puerto Rico. 55(4):518-19.

Benero, J. R., A. L. Collazo de Rivera, and L. M. I. de George. 1974. Studies on the preparation and shelf-life of soursop, tamarind and blended soursop-tamarind soft drinks. *Journal of Agriculture*. University of Puerto Rico. 58(1):99-104.

Leal, F. J. 1970. Notas sobre la guanabana (*Annona muricata*) en Venezuela. *Proceedings of the Tropical Regional American Society for Horticultural Science.* Mexico. 14:118-21.

Morton, J. F. 1966. The soursop or guanábana (*Annona muricata* Linn.) *Proceedings of the Florida State Horticultural Society*. 79:355-66.

Nakasone, H. Y. 1972. Production feasibility for soursop. *Hawaii Farm Science*. 21(1):10-11.

Payumo, E. M., L. M. Pilac, and P. L. Maniquis. 1965. The preparation and storage properties of canned guwayabano (*Annona muricata* L.) concentrate. *Philippine Journal of Science*. 94(2):161-69.

Sánchez-Nieva, F. 1970. Frozen soursop puree. *Journal of Agriculture*. University of Puerto Rico. 54(2):220-36.


### Research Contacts and Germ Plasm Supply

Food Technology Laboratory, University of Puerto Rico, Rio Piedras, Puerto Rico (J. R. Benero)

Hawaii Agricultural Experiment Station, Honolulu, Hawaii 96822, USA (H. Y. Makasone)

Jardín Botánico, Universidad del Valle, Cali, Colombia (V. M. Patiño)

University of the Philippines, College of Agriculture, Los Baños, Laguna, Philippines (R. V. Valmayor)

# UVILLA

Uvilla* (pronounced oo-vee-lya) is a small tree of the western Amazon (Brazil, Colombia, Peru). It produces large racemes of purple, grape-like fruit up to 4 cm wide, with a large pit and a sweet, white pulp. The fruit is consumed raw and is also made into wine. It grows in wet equatorial forests and could easily become pantropic. People living in the ecological environment where it grows have difficulty getting food. But uvilla is prolific; it fruits heavily and over a long period—3 months or so—during the wet season; few fruits (other than pineapple) grow well in similar wet equatorial forests. This tree is recommended for testing as a home-garden crop throughout the humid tropics.

A relatively fast grower, it begins to fruit in 3 years. The tree apparently has few, if any, enemies. The tree is cultivated singly around the Indians' houses. The fruit at the top of the tree ripens first. A forked branch is used to knock it off.

Uvilla exploitation has been totally neglected by science. It has never been the subject of an agronomic study, nor has any effort been made to establish plantations. It is proposed here as a topic for small-scale testing rather than for mass cultivation.

Related species, especially *P. sapida*, grow in the forest as wild trees. They bear edible fruit, but little else is known about them.

## LIMITATIONS AND SPECIAL REQUIREMENTS

Nothing whatever is known of the agronomic requirements of this plant. And nothing is known of the composition and nutritive value of the fruit, except that it is rich in sugars.

The skin is acrid and inedible and must be removed, but it peels off easily.

Uvilla is dioecious (pollen and fruit are born on different individual plants) and care must be taken in commercial orchards to plant enough polliniferous trees. In some regions, natives believe it is possible to distinguish the sex by examining the seeds. This needs experimental confirmation.

## RESEARCH NEEDS

A program for uvilla improvement should be initiated. It would not be costly. All known regional varieties and strains (some may be distinct species) should

*Pourouma cecropiaefolia* Mart. Also known as *imbaúba do vinho*, *uva de monte*, *caimarón*, Amazon grape, etc. Family: Moraceae.

Uvilla fruit. (J. Zarucchi)

be assembled in one nursery for development and hybridization of the best yielders, largest or sweetest fruit, fastest growers, etc.

Nutritionists should undertake research to identify the components and food value of the fruit.

Nothing is known of uvilla's industrial potential—its processing, preservation, or use as a flavoring. Exploratory investigation to identify the potential and problems could be rewarding.

## Selected Readings

Ducke, A. 1946. *Plantas de Cultura Precolombiana na Amazonia Brasileira. Notas Sobre las Especies ou Formas Espontâneas que Supostamente Ihes Teriam Dado Origem.* Boletin Tecnico No. 8. Instituto Agronômico do Norte, Belém, Brazil.

Macbride, J. F. 1960. Flora of Peru. *Fieldiana Botany*. 13(1, pt. 5). Field Museum of Natural History, Chicago, Illinois, USA.

Patiño, V. M. 1963. *Plantas Cultivadas y Animales Domesticos en America Equinoccial—Tomo I: Frutales*. Imprenta Departamental, Cali, Colombia.

Pérez-Arbeláez, E. 1956. *Plantas Utiles de Colombia*. 3rd Ed., Libreria Colombiana—Camacho Roldón Cía. (Ltda.), Bogotá, Colombia.

Romero-Castañeda, R. 1961. *Fruitas Silvestres de Colombia*. Vol. I. Author, Bogotá, Colombia.

Teixeira (sa Fonseca), E. 1954. *Frutas do Brasil*. Ministerio da Educaçao e Cultura. Instituto Nacional do Livro. Rio de Janeiro. Sedegra (Sociedad Editôra e Grafica Ltda.)

Uvilla tree in the Colombian Vaupés. (J. Zarucchi)

## Research Contacts and Germ Plasm Supply

Instituto Nacional de Pesquisas da Amazônia, Manaos, Brazil.

Ministerio de Agricultura, Bogotá, Colombia.

Universidad del Vale, Cali, Colombia (V. M. Patiño) [specimens in the Estación Agrícola de Palmira and Estación del Calima]

Universidad Nacional de la Amazonía Peruana. Facultad de Ciencias y Humanidades, Apartado 496, Iquitos, Perú. (C. S. Flores)

# V OILSEEDS

## BABASSÚ PALM

The babassú,* a palm native to the northern region of South America, produces an abundance of fruit containing up to 72 percent oil. Although it has been slightly commercialized, further research is necessary before its full potential can be realized.

Babassú kernels taste, smell, and look like coconut meat, but they contain more oil. Babassú is perhaps the only vegetable species that could replace coconut in the production of olein and stearin.

The babassú palm grows wild throughout more than 35 million acres of the Amazon basin. Before World War II, most of Brazil's babassú nuts (about 40,000 tons) were exported. But local processing for soap is expanding. Domestic production of oil rose from 6,000 tons in 1940 to 53,000 tons by 1965.

The potential output is enormous, but difficulties of cracking the hard, thick shell and collecting and transporting the nuts limit production.

Various levels of yield are reported for individual trees; a babassú palm may produce a ton of nuts a year, representing 90 kg of kernels. Palms on cultivated plantations have yielded 1,500 kg of nuts per ha.†

Babassú is a tall (as high as 20 m), majestic, fan-shaped palm with large, elegant, curved leaves that grow to 9 m long. Its bunches of oblong or conical fruit often reach up to 1 m in length. The bunches weigh from 14 to 90 kg and contain 200-600 fruits; 1-4 bunches per year are produced from the time the tree is 8-10 years old. The fruit (8-15 cm long and 5-9 cm thick) resembles a small coconut, weighs 150-200 grams, and contains 3-8 kernels. The kernels contain 60-70 percent oil and constitute 10 percent of the fruit's weight.

The kernel is surrounded by a pulp that is 10 percent starch, enclosed by a hard, woody shell nearly 12 mm thick, much like coconut shell. The pulp constitutes 20 percent of the weight of the fruit.

*Orbignya martiana Barb.-Rodr. and Orbignya oleifera Burret. Other Orbignya spp. may be useful in a similar way. Also known as babaçú, coco de macaco, aguassú. Family: Palmae.
†Markley. 1971. See Selected Readings.

The cross-section of a babassú nut gives an idea of the difficulty in shelling the nut to extract the kernel. (*Brazilian Bulletin*)

Babassú oil can be used for the same purposes as coconut oil—for example, for margarine, shortening, general edibles, toilet soap, fatty acids, and detergents. The oil is obtained by conventional methods of oilseed extraction. It is almost colorless, has an agreeable odor, and does not easily become rancid. After the oil is extracted, the remaining seed cake is used for animal feed. It contains up to 27 percent protein and resembles coconut cake in composition.

The hard shell (endocarp) makes an excellent fuel that is burned directly or converted to charcoal.

In general, native babassú grows in fairly pure stands in river valleys and deltas not subject to prolonged or permanent flooding, although it is also found in areas of high to low rainfall and dry to swampy conditions. It thrives in well-drained, alkaline or neutral soils, but it grows also in siliceous soils.

In Brazil the fruit ripens from July to November, then falls to the ground. After collection, the fruit is usually dried in the sun to facilitate removal of the shell from the kernel.

Two main species of babassú are found in Brazil, *Orbignya martiana* Barb. Rodr., which grows in the wet forest areas of the Amazon basin, and *Orbignya oleifera* Burret, which grows in the dry, semi-deciduous forests of Brazil outside Amazonia. The preceding descriptions are based on these species. However, other related palms offer commercial potential as oilseeds:

• *Orbignya cuatrecasana* A. Dugand grows in the Chocó region on the Pacific coast of Colombia. The seeds, known as *táparos* or *táparos grandes*, are eaten and used in other ways by the local inhabitants in much the same way that coconuts are used elsewhere.

• *Altalia speciosa* Mart. [formerly known as *Orbignya speciosa* (Mart.) Barb.-Rodr.] is found in tropical South America, especially Brazil. The fruit provides an excellent oil, though it is smaller and contains fewer seeds than the fruit of the species previously mentioned.

• *Orbignya cohune* Mart. The cohune palm grows in the rich lowlands of Mexico's Yucatán peninsula; Belize, Honduras; and Guatemala. Only small amounts are now harvested, but each palm bears from 1,000 to 2,000 fruits a year.

## LIMITATIONS AND SPECIAL REQUIREMENTS

As mentioned, the unusual hardness of the endocarp is the most serious obstacle to the increased use of babassú.

All species of babassú require tropical climates: warm temperatures, ample sunshine, and moist (but not waterlogged), fertile soils. *Orbignya martiana* prefers a very humid climate and is found usually in tropical rain-forest areas. *Orbignya oleifera* grows best in drier, semi-deciduous forests.

Although the kernel has the most important properties for commercial use, it accounts for only 10 percent of the nut. Therefore, it is not usually economical to transport whole fruits to a cracking and separating center, since 90 percent of the fruit has only incidental by-product value. Cracking and separating must be done locally.

If the kernels are not well dried, damage during decortication initiates enzyme action that will turn the oil rancid.

The palm is slow to mature. It begins to yield by 8 years and reaches full production in 10-15 years.

Just from existing stands in South America the potential output is enormous, but handicaps remain: labor for collecting the nuts is scarce; transport facilities are inadequate; and yields are low because the trees grow too densely.

## RESEARCH NEEDS

Machines have been developed that crack the shells and separate the seeds from the husks, but in most cases cracking is still done by hand and accounts for 57 percent of the cost. Research should be conducted to improve mechanization.

Tons of residue are discarded that should be put to productive use. The exterior of the nut, the fibrous epicarp, probably contains a wealth of new products.

Babassú palms. (H. S. Irwin)

Considerably more data should be acquired on the wild stands in South America. High-yield varieties with desirable characteristics should be propagated in a germ plasm bank in Brazil. The reasons for the great differential in the rate of production in the various regions should be investigated.

Though a few babassú plantations are well established, more agronomic data are needed before widespread plantation cultivation can be achieved.

## Selected Readings

Adames, G. E. 1943. Babassú. A hard nut to crack. *Agriculture in the Americas*. 3(10).
Eckey, E. W. 1954. *Vegetable Fats and Oils*. Reinhold, New York.
Godin, V. J. and P. C. Spensley. 1971. *TPI Crop and Product Digest No. 1 Oils and*

A close relative of babassú, the cohune palm grows in Central America. Like babassú, it has huge bunches of fruit as shown here. (W. H. Hodge)

*Oilseeds.* The Tropical Products Institute, London. (Available from: Publications Section, Tropical Products Institute, 56/62 Gray's Inn Road, London WC1X 8LU, England.)

Inmay, H. de 1949. The "Cusi" palm, *O. phalerate* and "babassú" oil. A potential industry from the forests of Bolivia. *Revista de Agricultura.* 6(5):29-42. (Cochabamba, Bolivia).

Markley, K. S. 1971. The babassú oil palm of Brazil. *Economic Botany.* 25(3):267-304.

Ministry of Agriculture, Brazil. 1955. *O Babaçú.* Publication Ser. Estud. e Ensaios, No. 8.

Pinto, R. W. 1951. Babassú–Brazil's wonder nut. *Foreign Commerce Weekly.* 45, Oct:3-4.

Planejamento da utilização do babaçú. 1952. *Revista de Quimica Industrial* (Rio de Janeiro). 21(242):14.

Poliakoff, J. 1957. Brazilian oilseeds. *Oléagineux.* 12(3):172-4.

Rizzini, C. T. 1963. Sôbre a distinção e a distribuição das duas espécies de babacú (*Orbignya*). *Revista Brasileira de Geografia* (Rio de Janeiro). 25(3):313-26.

Sadaba, R. M. 1953. The importance and economic future of the babaçú palm. *Boletin Oleiculture Internacional* 3:23-31.

Silva, S. A. Ferreira da. 1971. *Primeira contribuição ao catálogo sistemático de plantas Brasilerias produtoras de óleo, cêra e resina. 1° Parte, Monocotiledôneas.* (First contribution to the systematic catalogue of Brazilian oil, wax, and resin-producing plants. 1st part, Monocotyledons.) Centro de Tecnologia Agrícola e Alimentar, Departmento Nacional de Pesquisa Agropecuária, Ministério da Agricultura, Rio de Janeiro, Brazil.

Smith, N. 1974. *Agouti and Babassú.* Oryx. 12(5):581-2. The Fauna Preservation Society.

Souza Rezende, E. J. de 1964. Approveitamento econômico de babaçú. *Revista de Quimica Industrial.* 33:25.

Weiss, M. 1955. La babassú, richesse national du Brésil. *Oléagineux.* 10(12):839-43.

## Research Contacts and Germ Plasm Supply

Institute of Industrial Technology, Belo Horizonte, Brazil (A. V. Filho)
University of Maranhão, São Luíz, Maranhão, Brazil

# BUFFALO GOURD

Demands for edible oil and protein in arid lands are increasing. Until recently, wild gourds belonging to the squash family, Cucurbitaceae, have been overlooked as a potential source of oil and protein for livestock and humans. Several of these are highly drought-tolerant, particularly the buffalo gourd.*

*Cucurbita foetidissima* HBK. Also known as buffalo gourd, chilicote, or mock orange. Family: Cucurbitaceae.

Harvesting these two buffalo gourd plants growing wild near Snyder, Texas, yielded 1.3 kg of dry seed, despite arid conditions, lack of care, and lack of agronomic improvement. (L. C. Curtis)

On barren land the buffalo gourd may match the performance of traditional protein and oil sources such as peanuts and sunflowers, which require more water. But little research has been conducted, and the buffalo gourd is not yet commercially cultivated anywhere. Much research, particularly into the nutritional efficiency of the oil and protein, still remains to be done.

The buffalo gourd is a vigorous perennial. It grows wild on wastelands in the deserts of Mexico and the southwestern United States, and produces an abundant crop of fruit containing seed rich in oil and protein. Its large, fleshy, dahlia-like tubers grow as deep as 5 m to obtain and store water. The plant is covered with a dull, wax coating. It produces yellow, hard-shelled, spherical fruit (to 8 cm diameter) containing pulp and flat, white seeds 12 mm long and 7 mm wide. The fruit can be mechanically harvested and the flesh dries so completely in arid environments that the seed inside can be threshed out.

Each fruit of the buffalo gourd contains about 12 grams of seed and, on the basis of 60 fruits to the plant, 1 hectare of plants can produce 2.5 tons of seed. The seed contains 30-35 percent protein and up to 34 percent oil.* These (estimated) yields compare favorably with other oil- and protein-bearing crops such as soybeans and peanuts.

The seeds can be crushed to obtain the edible polyunsaturated oil for food and industrial use. The pulp from undried fruit is used for cattle feed.

The buffalo gourd's enormous root can weigh as much as 30 kg (70 percent moisture) after just two growing seasons. It is filled with starch and in

*Jacks, Hensarling, and Yetsu. 1972. See Selected Readings.

addition to its other uses buffalo gourd is now becoming recognized as a root crop. The roots (as well as the leaves and fruit) contain bitter-tasting glycosides; however, the starch can be separated from them by soaking in a dilute salt solution.

The plants are long lived; some are reportedly over 40 years old. They are highly resistant to cucumber beetle and squash bug. The plants can be propagated asexually from nodal roots: if the long, running vines are stapled to the soil and watered, a fresh root starts. This cloning process produces new generations rapidly. Within 2 years, thousands of genetically identical offspring can be ready to plant.

The buffalo gourd has been used by North American Indians for centuries. They used the seeds for food and soapy extracts of the fruit pulp and vine for washing clothes and cleaning hides.

One research project on the buffalo gourd, at the Arid Land Agricultural Development Institute in Lebanon, is hybridizing varieties to obtain seeds that produce plants that mature more quickly and give a higher yield. The institute is also working to develop seeds with higher oil and protein content and a purer oil that can be stored without turning rancid. Recently, some of the highest-yielding gourds have been found to be male-sterile, opening vistas of simplified replication.

Buffalo gourd growing wild in the desert near White Sands, New Mexico. (L. C. Curtis)

One half of a 3-year-old buffalo gourd root. This specimen weighed 145 kg. Although this was produced by a plant growing under extremely arid conditions, the 70 kg of starch it contains is equivalent to the amount produced by a score of potato plants grown under good conditions. (L. C. Curtis)

## LIMITATIONS AND SPECIAL REQUIREMENTS

Buffalo gourds require long periods of warm, dry weather for optimum growth. They are sensitive to frost and intolerant of wet, poorly drained soil.

Great yield differences occur among individual plants: some are essentially barren, some prolific. The size of the fruit varies. Some variations are undoubtedly due to seasonal fluctuations, others are genetic. Some plants have a preponderance of male, some of female flowers.

As already mentioned, it is not known how the oil and the pressed cake containing the protein will compare with other oils and proteins as food for humans and livestock. The possibility that the meal or protein might be inedible must be investigated by extended feeding trials.

Buffalo gourd protein—like other plant proteins—is low in lysine and the sulfur-containing amino acids.

Buffalo gourd under cultivation, Lebanon.  (L. C. Curtis)

## RESEARCH NEEDS

Experimental plantings, selection, and breeding are needed in many new regions.

The meal has a high phytic acid content, and extensive feeding tests should be undertaken to determine whether excessive saponins or other toxic substances are present.

More information is needed on water requirements and other agronomic parameters.

### Selected Readings

Ba-Amer, M. A., and W. P. Bemis. 1968. Fruit and seed development in *Cucurbita foetidissima. Economic Botany*. 22(3):297-9.

Bemis, W. P., L. C. Curtis, C. W. Weber, J. W. Berry, and J. M. Nelson. 1975. *The Buffalo Gourd* (Cucurbita foetidissima *HBK*): *A Potential Crop for the Production of Protein, Oil, and Starch on Arid Lands*. Office of Agriculture, Technical Assistance Bureau, Agency for International Development, Washington, D.C. 20523, USA.

Berry, J. W., W. P. Bemis, C. W. Weber, and T. Philips. Cucurbit root starches: Isolation and some properties of starches from *Cucurbita foetidissima* HBK and *C. digitata* Gray. *Journal of Agriculture and Food Chemistry*. (In Press)

Bolley, D. S., R. H. McCormack, and L. C. Curtis. 1950. Utilization of the seeds of the wild perennial gourds. *Journal of the American Oil Chemists' Society*. 27:571-4.

Curtis, L. C. 1972. *An Attempt to Domesticate a Wild, Perennial, Xerophytic Gourd,* Cucurbita foetidissima, *Progress Report No. 1*. The Ford Foundation, Beirut, Lebanon.

Curtis, L. C., and H. Gómez, C. 1974. *Cucurbita foetidissima*, una fuente potencial de aceite y proteina en zonas áridas. *Boletín Técnico 4*. 12(1). Centro Nacional de Investigacion para el Desarrollo de Zonas Aridas, Saltillo, Coahuila, Mexico.

Jacks, T. H., T. P Hensarling, and L. Y. Yatsu. 1972. Cucurbit seeds: I. Characterizations and uses of oils and proteins, a review. *Economic Botany*. 26(2):135-41.

Shahani, H. S., F. G. Dollear, K. S. Markley, and J. R. Quinby. 1951. The buffalo gourd, a potential oilseed crop of the southwestern drylands. *Journal of the American Oil Chemists' Society*. 28:90-5.

### Research Contacts and Germ Plasm Supply

The Arid Lands Agricultural Development Program, The Ford Foundation, Beirut, Lebanon

Centro Nacional de Investigacion para el Desarrollo de Zonas Aridas, Saltillo, Coahuila, Mexico (H. Gomez, C.)

Department of Agricultural Biochemistry, University of Arizona, Tucson, Arizona 85721, USA (W. P. Bemis)

L. C. Curtis & Son, Inc., Watkinsville, Georgia 30677, USA (L. C. Curtis)

U.S.D.A., Southern Regional Research Center, P.O. Box 19687, New Orleans, Louisiana 70179, USA (R. J. Jacks)

# CARYOCAR SPECIES

*Caryocar** species, tropical New World trees, are abundant in the Amazon basin, the Guianas, and central Brazil. Their seeds are an excellent source of edible oil. Oil production from these species could be greatly increased and industrialized. But this is a long-term project requiring considerable research.

In the 19th century, Sir Henry Wickham, the man who introduced rubber trees to Malaya, gave equal emphasis to the potential of *Caryocar villosum* and of rubber when he sent the seeds of both trees from Brazil to Malaya. But caryocar did not receive equal attention by the recipients. By 1952 it was reported that the trees still surviving from Wickham's seed were sadly neglected, and that there had been no postwar production of nuts or oil there.

Caryocar fruit, like those of oil palm, yields two edible oils—one from the pericarp and one from the kernel. In texture and flavor, caryocar kernels are said to be the best edible nuts in the tropics.

There are 15 caryocar species. The best known, *Caryocar brasiliense* or pequí, is a medium-sized tree that flourishes in the Planalto of Central Brazil. A closely related species, also showing great promise, is *Caryocar villosum*. *Caryocar brasiliense* probably has greater potential because it is a smaller tree and therefore easier to harvest. It grows in marginal, low-quality soil, where few other economically useful crops will grow. *Caryocar brasiliense*, flourishing in the *cerrados* of central Brazil, is a low tree with beautiful yellow or white flowers. The fruit (about the size of an orange) contains an oily pulp and kernel that are used for food. So far, they have been employed only in home cooking. The fruit is made into a tasty liqueur, well known in Brazil.

The fruit is surrounded by a fibrous husk (mesocarp) similar to coconut husk. Ten percent of the fruit is a starch. The large, fleshy fruit, weighing as much as 0.4 kg, is surrounded by a shell (endocarp), which, like coconut shell, is used for fuel, either directly or after conversion to charcoal. Inside are 1-4 kidney-shaped, brown kernels similar to Brazil nuts, coated with a pale yellow fat that provides oil. It is a sweet oil and is an excellent substitute for cooking fat and butter. The oil is composed largely of glyceride esters of palmitic and oleic acids. Like the palm oil that it resembles, it can be used for similar purposes. It is easily bleached.

The kernels have a thick shell almost impossible to crack. They, too (like oil palm kernels), contain an oil highly prized by the indigenous populations of northern South America.

*e.g., *Caryocar brasiliense* Camb. Also known as pequí or piquí in Brazil; and *Caryocar villosum*, known as piqui-á in Brazil. Family: Caryocaraceae.

Souari nuts from *Caryocar glabrum*. (Field Museum, Chicago)

By the time they are 9 years old, the trees reach a height of 10 m; the spread of their branches equals their height. The wood from some caryocar species (e.g., *Caryocar villosum*) is so durable that it is used in shipbuilding.

Other caryocar species worthy of commercial consideration include:

• *Caryocar amgydaliferum* Mutis. This tree grows in northern South America and produces seeds that are a source of pleasant-tasting sawatre or suari fat, used in food.

• *Caryocar glabrum* Perr. A tree of the Guianas, it is known also as soapwood.

• *Caryocar nuciferum* L. It is a tall tree that grows in Brazil and the Guianas, and is also cultivated in the West Indies. A product of the tree is suari nuts or butternuts, whose edible oil is exported.

• *Caryocar tomentosum* Willd. A large tree of the Guianas, it is also known as suari tree.


## LIMITATIONS AND SPECIAL REQUIREMENTS

The caryocar tree has never been agronomically researched, but it appears that economic considerations are the only real obstacle to success of the tree as a tropical crop. Even initial investigation might produce cost-cutting measures.

The ripe fruits must be treated as soon as they are harvested, because enzymes cause free fatty acids to develop during storage.


## RESEARCH NEEDS

A caryocar seed bank should be developed to supply interested agricultural organizations throughout the world. Horticultural requirements must be determined.

All economic aspects of harvesting, processing, and marketing require study.


### Selected Readings

Barradas, M. M. 1972. Informações sobre floração frutificação de ispersão do Piquí *Caryocar brasiliensis* Camb. (Caryocaraceae). *Ciencia e Cultura*. 24(11):1063-8. (Available from the author, see Contacts list.)

Barradas, M. M. 1973. Morfología do fruto e da semente de *Caryocar brasiliense* (Piquí) em várias fases de desenvolvimento. *Revista de Biologia* (Lisb.) 9(1-4):69-84. (Available from the author, see Contacts list.)

George, C. D. V. 1929. Piqui-á fruit oils. *Malayan Agriculture Journal*. 17:166.

Handro, W., and M. M. Barradas. 1971. Sôbre os óleos do fruto e da semente do Piqui–*Caryocar brasiliense* Camb. *III Simpósio sobre o cerrado*. pp. 110-13. (Editôra Blücher, São Paulo) This paper contains an analysis of the oil content of the fruit.

Howes, R. N. 1953. *Nuts: Their Production and Everyday Uses*. Faber and Faber, Ltd., London.

Killy, C. L. 1942. Two new species of Caryocaraceae from northern South America. *Tropical Woods*. 72:16-18.

Lane, E. V. 1957. Piqui-á–potential source of vegetable oil for an oil-starving world. *Economic Botany*. 11(3):187-207.

Prance, G. T., and M. F. da Silva. 1973. Caryocaraceae. *Flora Neotropica*. 12:1-75.

## Research Contacts and Germ Plasm Supply

Instituto Biológico, Caixa Postal 7119, São Paulo, Brazil. (M. M. Barradas)
Instituto Nacional de Pesquisas de Amazonia, Manaos, Brazil
New York Botanical Gardens, Bronx, New York 10458, USA (G. Prance)

# JESSENIA POLYCARPA

*Jessenia polycarpa** is a little-known palm that produces oil closely resembling olive oil. It grows abundantly in some lowland areas of the Amazon region of Venezuela and Colombia. Its extraordinarily large and heavy fruit clusters are comparable to those of the African oil palm. Though much used in its homeland, the plant has never been cultivated; however, current olive oil prices make the jessenia well worth investigating as a potential commercial source of edible oil.

The purple fruit, 3 cm long, has a thin, oily, edible pulp enclosing a fibrous husk that surrounds a horny seed. The pulp constitutes almost 40 percent (dry weight basis) of the whole fruit; it is approximately 50 percent oil. Adult palms average two fruit clusters per year or 30 kg of fruit, from which 22 kg of oil (24 liters) can be extracted.

The yellow oil from the pulp is sold in markets in Colombia. It is equally satisfactory for food, soap, or cosmetics. The milky residue from oil extraction (called yucuta) is consumed as a beverage. The seeds are eaten mainly by the poor.

Feather-leaved *Jessenia polycarpa* grows in dry soil above flood level in the Amazon basin. Another palm, *Astrocaryum*, grows along river banks flooded for 5 months of the year. It also bears fruit in edible oil. If *Astrocaryum* were grown in conjunction with jessenia, both types of land, which commonly occur together, could be utilized.

Another species *Jessenia bataua* (Mart) Burret, is a medium-sized palm that grows in the states of Para and Amazonas in Brazil, in Colombia, and in the Orinoco River Valley and the Gulf of Paria in Venezuela. The pulp contains 18-24 percent oil, which is yellow-green in color. The oil, of high quality and

---

*Jessenia polycarpa* Karst. Also known as seje, seje grande, coroba, milpesos (Colombia) and jagua (Venezuela). Family: Palmae.

almost identical to olive oil, is obtained by boiling the macerated fruit in water. Its production is very limited at present.

*Jessenia weberbaueri* Burret of Peru bears exceptionally large fruit (to 4 cm long with seeds 2.5 cm long, 1.5 cm wide).

A jessenia palm in the Vaupés of Colombia. (J. Zarucchi)

## LIMITATIONS AND SPECIAL REQUIREMENTS

Very little is known about any *Jessenia* species or their products. Such basic information as the number of years required for the plant to mature and bear seed has not yet been determined.

## RESEARCH NEEDS

All species of *Jessenia* should be checked for their oil production and quality. Testing *Jessenia polycarpa* (or another species if it proves superior) under plantation conditions is essential. If a plantation culture could be developed, it would be the key to successful utilization of the plant.

### Selected Readings

Macbride, J. F. 1960. Flora of Peru. *Fieldiana Botany*. 13(2, pt. 1):379-80. Field Museum of Natural History, Chicago, Illinois, USA.

Pérez-Arbeláez, E. 1956. *Plantas Útiles de Colombia*. 3rd ed. Libreria Colombiana, Camacho Roldán Cía (Ltda), Bogotá, Colombia.

Ranghel Galindo, A. 1945 La palmera milpes o seje de la Amazonia colombiana *Agricultura Tropical*. 6:40-43 (Photocopies available from R. E. Schultes, Botanical Museum, Harvard University, Oxford Street, Cambridge, Massachusetts, 02138, USA.)

Uphof, J. C. 1968. *Dictionary of Economic Plants*. S-H Service Agency, Inc., Riverside, New Jersey, 08075, USA.

### Research Contacts and Germ Plasm Supply

Jardin Botanico, "Joaquin Antonio Uribe," Medelin, Colombia (A. Arango, Director) Ministerio de Agricultura, Bogotá, Colombia.

# JOJOBA

Jojoba* (pronounced ho-ho-ba) is a hardy shrub that grows in arid regions of northern Mexico and the southwestern United States. Its seeds contain a liquid "wax" (esters of fatty acids and alcohols) that has impressive industrial potential.

It is difficult to produce synthetic liquid wax commercially. Since the endangered sperm whale is the only natural source at present, the jojoba plant may, in time, become the only source of liquid wax. Jojoba oil may

*Simmondsia chinensis* (Link) Schneider. Family: Buxaceae.

Jojoba seeds, oil, and the very hard wax that is obtained by hydrogenating jojoba oil. (E. Battaglia)

eventually replace sperm oil and save the species by making it uneconomical to hunt sperm whales.

Industry uses sperm oil in lubricants that must withstand extreme pressures—for example, in machinery gears and automobile transmissions. Sperm whale oil is so valuable to industry in the United States that it has been classified as a strategic material and stockpiled against national emergencies. The liquid wax from jojoba may provide an economically attractive alternative.

Some other plants yield saturated, solid waxes as coatings on seeds, fruits, leaves, and stems, but jojoba oil is the only unsaturated, liquid wax readily extractable in large quantities from a plant source.

Jojoba cultivation and processing, the manufacture of jojoba products, and the utilization of by-products might help impoverished peoples in arid lands to become economically self-supporting.

The jojoba plant tolerates extreme desert temperatures: daily highs of 35°-45°C shade readings are common during the summer. A true drought-resistant desert shrub, it thrives under soil and moisture conditions not suitable for most agricultural crops.

Five hundred mm of rainfall a year is sufficient to support productive stands of jojoba; even 100 mm may produce a light crop of seed. The shrub has been known to survive as long as a year with no rainfall at all. A cash crop of jojoba would not significantly deplete scarce water supplies, which are now in great demand to sustain increased population and cultivation of water-consuming crops such as cotton and sorghum. Jojoba requires water during winter and spring months to set its flowers and seeds. Its summer requirements are low in contrast to most crops that, in arid regions, need water when it is most scarce to protect them from drought. Jojoba also appears to be fairly salt tolerant: one tested variety, Vista, showed no detrimental effect on growth or flower production at a soil-water salinity of about 7,000 mg per liter.*

Frequently stunted to a height of 60-90 cm by the harshness of its environment or heavy browsing by wildlife or livestock, jojoba grows as high as 2-3 m in well-watered sites. An evergreen, it has thick, leathery, bluish-green leaves and brown nut-like fruit. Its natural lifespan appears to be more than 100 years and may exceed 200 years. Jojoba is a rugged plant that can regenerate lost limbs and survive harsh treatment.

Jojoba seeds contain about 50 percent liquid wax. The wax can be obtained in high purity by pressing or by using a solvent to extract the seeds, using conventional oilseed equipment. It often requires little refining for use in lubricants. It is very slow to turn rancid. Its viscosity, flash point, and fire point are similar to those of sperm whale oil. Perhaps the most important property of jojoba wax is that it is undamaged by repeated heating to high temperatures and reportedly does not change viscosity after repeated temperature changes.

The wax has been suggested for use in a variety of products ranging from linoleum to detergents to pharmaceuticals. Its stability in terms of oxidation and rancidity make it particularly attractive for use in cosmetics and other products.

After the wax has been extracted, the residual seed meal contains up to 35 percent protein. It has an unusual chemical that suppresses the appetite of laboratory rats, but may become acceptable, after processing, for livestock feed, especially in the feed-short arid regions where jojoba grows.

In addition, the wax can be easily hydrogenated to produce a solid, hard, white wax, with important potential for use in polishing waxes, carbon paper, and a host of other products. It may be a suitable substitute for carnauba and beeswax, whose prices have recently increased sharply.

## LIMITATIONS AND SPECIAL REQUIREMENTS

A serious limitation to the development of jojoba is the lack of high-yield varieties. Seed now available is variable and produces non-uniform plants with uneven yields. Cuttings (which would circumvent this) have proven difficult to root.

*Yermanos, D. M., Francois L. E., and Tammadoni, T. 1968. *Economic Botany*. 22.

Jojoba bushes covering the hill slopes in the Sonoran desert near Tucson, Arizona. (University of Arizona)

Harvesting jojoba in a 10-year-old plantation at Bilat, Israel. This area receives about 230 mm annual rainfall, but without any irrigation some of the best plants yeild 3 kg of fruit in a single harvest. (M. Forti)

From planting until the first harvest takes 4-5 years. Investment money is, therefore, tied up for a long time before income is realized. Because 7 to 8 years are required to achieve full yield potential, jojoba research must be planned on a long-term basis.

Jojoba bushes are either staminate (male) or pistillate (female). Only the pistillate bears seed. At present one cannot distinguish the sex of seedlings until they flower. Several seeds must be planted at each site to ensure that enough pistillate plants will be available. Most of the staminate plants are removed at maturity leaving only enough to pollinate the pistillate plants.

Jojoba plants, especially when young, are sensitive to frost.

## RESEARCH NEEDS

Jojoba will need an integrated research and development program designed to include the following:

• Development of large-scale jojoba plantations for technical and economic evaluation;

• Selection and breeding for productivity, hermaphroditism (both sexes on the same bush), cold resistance, multiple annual yields, early maturation, and a shape that facilitates harvest;

• Agronomic investigation to define factors influencing growth and yield such as altitude, temperature, moisture regime, fertilizers, plant-spacing, ratio of male to female plants, and soil types;

• Development of new uses for jojoba wax and its derivatives, and testing products for their importance and value to industry;

• Detoxification of jojoba meal for use as animal feed;

• Research to find sex-linked characteristics that would allow early sex identification of a seed or seedling;

• Development of commercial methods of repetitive propagation for rapid production of desirable varieties. This would make possible large plantations of the uniform, selected varieties most useful to agriculture and industry.

### Selected Readings

Daugherty, P. M., H. H. Sineath, and T. A. Wastler. 1953. Industrial raw materials of plant origin. IV:A survey of *Simmondsia chinensis. Economic Botany*. 12:296-306. *Georgia Institute of Technology, Engineering Experiment Station*, Bulletin 17:1-36.

Gentry, H. S. 1958. The natural history of jojoba (*Simmondsia chinensis*) and its cultural aspects. *Economic Botany*. 12(3):261-95.

Haase, E. F., and W. G. McGinnies, eds., 1972. *Jojoba and its uses. An International Conference June, 1972*. Office of Arid Lands Studies, College of Earth Sciences, University of Arizona, Tucson, Arizona 85719, USA.

*Jojoba Happenings*, a newsletter, is published four times a year by the Office of Arid Lands Studies, University of Arizona, in cooperation with an informal "International Committee for Jojoba Development." Interested individuals can receive this without charge by writing to: The Jojoba Coordinator, Office of Arid Lands Studies, The University of Arizona, 1201 East Speedway, Tucson, Arizona 85719, USA.

Mirov, N. T. 1952. Simmondsia or jojoba, a problem in economic botany. *Economic Botany*. 6(1):41-7.

National Academy of Sciences. 1975. *Products From Jojoba: A Promising New Crop for Arid Lands*. Washington, D.C. (For ordering information, see page 187.)

Sherbrooke, W. C., and E. F. Haase. 1974. *Jojoba: A Wax-producing Shrub of the Sonoran Desert. Literature Review and Annotated Bibliography*. University of Arizona, Office of Arid Lands Studies, Tucson, Arizona 85719, USA.

## Research Contacts and Germ Plasm Supply

Department of Agronomy, University of California, Riverside, California 92502, USA (D. M. Yermanos).

Department of Geography, University of California, Berkeley, California 94720, USA (N. T. Mirov).

Desert Botanical Garden, Phoenix, Arizona 85010, USA (H. S. Gentry)

National Academy of Sciences, 2101 Constitution Avenue, N.W., Washington, D.C. 20418, USA (N. D. Vietmeyer).

Research and Development Authority, Ben-Gurion University of the Negev, P.O.B. 1025, Beer-Sheva 84110, Israel (M. Forti).

United States Department of Agriculture, Beltsville, Maryland 20705, USA (H. Hyland).

University of Arizona, Office of Arid Lands Studies, Tucson, Arizona 85719, USA (J. Johnson).

# VI  FORAGE

## ACACIA ALBIDA

*Acacia albida** is a leguminous tree, widespread in tropical and southern Africa (extending to Cyprus, Israel, and Lebanon), which, curiously, bears its leaves through the dry season and sheds them at the start of the wet season. The reason for the tree's peculiar behavior—in full leaf when most other plants are leafless—is not fully understood. *Acacia albida* has great promise as a forage plant in areas with a prolonged dry season.

Its foliage is a valuable fodder for all types of stock. The young leaves and shoots are usually avidly browsed. Livestock that eat *Acacia albida* remain in good condition during the dry season when it is often the only green growth available. The tree is often lopped and branches carried to the camels, cattle, sheep, and goats. The pods, too, are eaten by livestock, especially cattle, and also by elephants, antelope, and baboons. The nutritional value does not deteriorate on drying (which is the case with many other acacias), so *Acacia albida* is fed dry in many parts of Africa. In the Sudan, trees produce an average of 135 kg of pods per tree. The yield from a stand of 12 trees in the Sudan has been calculated to be 200 kg of crude protein from the pods alone. This compares favorably with 180 kg of crude protein from a crop of unshelled groundnuts. The two crops can be, and are, grown together, since the groundnuts (and other crops) are grown during the wet season when the *Acacia albida* is leafless.

*Acacia albida* is a large, thorny tree. It is sometimes shrubby, but grows up to 25 m high if allowed to grow uncoppiced. In West Africa, it is generally left standing in the arable lands. Leaf-litter decay and excreta from grazing animals during the dry season enrich the soil, which has resulted in greatly increased yields. There is, as yet, no evidence of any appreciable benefit from nitrogen fixation by the roots.

The seeds contain up to 27 percent crude protein and are eaten by people in Rhodesia during times of famine. The seeds are boiled to loosen the skin and

---

*Acacia albida* Del. Also known as *Faidherbia albida* (Del.) A. Chev., apple-ring acacia, winter thorn, camel thorn. Family: Leguminosae.

then reboiled to separate the kernels. A mature tree can produce more than a million seeds a year.

*Acacia albida* pods may be mixed with maize and groundnut meal for food or combined with hay and succulents for fodder.

In southern and eastern Africa, *Acacia albida* is always found in riparian communities, but in West Africa it also grows away from river banks and watercourses—often in cultivated lands. Its growth patterns vary widely; sometimes the trees grow singly, sometimes in groups, whose upper branches grow together forming a canopy. Although it can be found in altitudes up to 1,800 m in Uganda, and as high as 2,300 - 2,500 m in the Sudan, it is more usually found below 1,200 m. In areas where the soil is permanently moist, the tree is likely to remain green for longer periods than in those areas where the soils are only seasonally moist. Where there is a bimodal rainfall pattern, there are two flowering periods and two flushes of leaf per year.

The sapwood is dirty white. The soft, yellowish-white heartwood is subject to attack by borers and termites. Although it is easy to work, it springs and twists after sawing, even when the wood is seasoned. The old bark is rich in tannin (28 percent), the roots and pods are not (5 percent). In northern Nigeria, the pounded bark makes a packing material for pack saddles for oxen and donkeys. In West Africa and Tanzania the tree yields a gum of good quality.

In the savanna country of Ethiopia, *Acacia albida's* broad canopy of protein-rich leaves and pods provide shade and feed for livestock in the dry season. (H. C. D. deWitt)

# LIMITATIONS AND SPECIAL REQUIREMENTS

*Acacia albida* trees are thorny. Some pods are reputed to taint milk when fed to dairy cows.

The seeds, as in many other species of *Acacia*, are sometimes heavily infested with bruchid beetles. The seedlings are especially susceptible to insect damage, but no more so than many other native species.

# RESEARCH NEEDS

*Acacia albida* deserves further investigation throughout its natural habitat to determine ecological demands and limits such as soil, climate, and altitude. Experimental plantings in arid regions of Central and South America, Asia, and Australia should be conducted to determine:

- The amount of forage produced and its nutrient value;
- The effect on livestock of protracted feeding;
- The techniques for propagating and cultivating the plant;
- Its potential for coppicing (regeneration via new shoots);
- The effect of browsing on the plant;
- The effect of the thorns on animals (camels don't seem to care);
- The effect of nitrogen fixation; and
- Its potential to fix nitrogen.

## Selected Readings

Codd, L. E. W. 1951. Trees and shrubs of the Kruger national park. *Botanical Survey Memoirs. 26.* Department of Agriculture, Cape Town, Union of South Africa.

Dalziel, J. M. 1937. *Useful Plants of West Tropical Africa.* Crown Agents for the Colonies, London. p. 202.

Hunting Technical Services (G. E. Wickens). 1968. *Land and Water Resources Survey of the Jebel Marra Area, Republic of the Sudan.* Reconnaissance Vegetation Survey. *Acacia albida* Del.—a general survey (with special reference to observations made in the U.N.S.F. Jebel Marra Project). Volume 2, Appendix IV, pp. 24-72. Food & Agriculture Organization of the United Nations, Rome. (Order number: LA:SF/SUD/17.)

Irvine, F. R. 1961. *Woody Plants of Ghana.* Oxford University Press, London.

Radwanski, S. A., and G. E. Wickens. 1967. The ecology of *Acacia albida* on mantle soils in Zalingei, Jebel Marra, Sudan. *Journal of Applied Ecology*, 4:569-79.

Watt, J. M., and M. G. Breyer-Brandwijk. 1962. *Medicinal and Poisonous Plants of Southern and Eastern Africa.* 2nd Ed. E. & S. Livingstone Ltd., Edinburgh.

Wickens, G. E. 1969. A study of *Acacia albida* Del. (Mimosoideae). *Kew Bulletin.* 23:181-202.

### Research Contacts and Germ Plasm Supply

The Herbarium, Royal Botanic Gardens, Kew, Richmond, Surrey, England (G. E. Wickens)

Laboratory for Plant Taxonomy, and Geography, 37 General Foulkesweg, Wageningen, The Netherlands (H.C.D. deWitt)

# BROSIMUM ALICASTRUM

Wherever it grows in quantity, *Brosimum alicastrum** is much used as stock feed, especially during dry seasons when other forage is scarce. Yet, outside its natural range, little attention has been given to its economic potential. The tree could be an important forage source for any tropical area that suffers feed shortages in dry seasons.

Native to southern Mexico and to much of Central America, *Brosimum alicastrum* is also fairly common in western Jamaica and western Cuba. Although indigenous to moist forests, it is extremely tolerant of drought. In Guatemala, Belize, and the Yucatan peninsula it is often the principal feed for stock during drier months.

Cattle appear to enjoy the leaves and branch tips; the abundant fruit serves as pig feed. The fruit's sweet pericarp and its chestnut-like seeds are eaten by humans. The seeds taste somewhat like potatoes and are eaten raw, boiled, and roasted. They are also reduced to a meal that is mixed with maize meal to make tortillas, or are baked with green plantain. The seeds are gathered by the Mayans for making their native bread when stocks of maize run low.

The trees can be tapped and the free-flowing, milky latex mixed with chicle or drunk like cow's milk. A related species, *Brosimum utile*, is the "cow-tree" of Venezuela (made famous by Humboldt) which furnishes a potable, milk-like latex.

*Brosimum alicastrum* wood is white, dense, hard, and fine grained. It is sometimes used for construction and carpentry in Yucatan.

The commercial value of chicle (the basis of chewing gum) spurred development of logging camps in the Yucatan forests. *Brosimum alicastrum* foliage is still used as fodder for the mules that carry the *chicleros* (and archaeologists). At each camp, trees are felled and the branches lopped off so

---

**Brosimum alicastrum* Sw. Also known as ramon, capomo, etc. Family: Moraceae.

*Brosimum alicastrum* used as an ornamental in Mérida, Mexico. Because its deep roots can always reach water, the tree remains green even during dry seasons. (F. J. Cárdenas Patrón)

that the animals can browse the leaves, nuts, and twigs, which they eat eagerly. Groves of large *Brosimum alicastrum* trees are considered a source of livestock feed equal to the best pastures.

## LIMITATIONS AND SPECIAL REQUIREMENTS

*Brosimum alicastrum* trees grow to heights of 20-30 m; the trunk may attain a diameter of 1 m. If managed for fodder, the plant can be maintained as a small tree, but expert tree climbers are required to lop off the branches of mature, unmanaged trees.

## RESEARCH NEEDS

The cultural requirements of *Brosimum alicastrum* and its adaptability to new regions need testing. Reportedly, the tree can be grown from seeds, cuttings, or air layers. Experiments are needed to determine whether the trees can be closely planted and regularly coppiced. The fodder yield of coppiced trees should be determined and compared with that of other drought-tolerant fodder plants.

Seeds and leaves should be studied to determine the nutritional basis for their feed and food values.

There are three named varieties in Mexico. These and other types should be collected and evaluated as feed and food sources.

Because *Brosimum alicastrum* is related to *Artocarpus communis*, the breadfruit of the Pacific Islands, and because fermented breadfruit paste has a remarkably long shelf life, a study of the fermentation and storage behavior of *Brosimum alicastrum* seeds and fruit pericarp could be of great importance.

### Selected Readings

Martínez, M. 1959. *Las Plantas Medicinales de Mexico.* 4th ed. Ediciones Botas, Mexico., D. F., Mexico.

Pennington, T. D., and J. Sarukhan. 1968. *Arboles Tropicales de Mexico.* FAO and Instituto Nacional de Investigaciones Forestales, Mexico, D. F., Mexico.

Souza-Novelo, N. 1950. *Plantas Alimentícias y Plantas de Condimento que Viven en Yucatán.* Instituto Técnico, Agrícola Henequenero. Mérida, Yucatán, Mexico.

Standley, P. C., and J. Steyermark. 1946. Flora of Guatemala. IV. *Fieldiana Botany.* 24(4):493. Field Museum of Natural History, Chicago, Illinois, USA.

Leaves and pods of *Brosimum alicastrum* provide good-quality, year-round, livestock feed, which is a valuable resource during dry seasons. (F. J. Cárdenas Patrón)

## Research Contacts and Germ Plasm Supply

Químico Biólogo, Calle 57 #474-C, Central Pediátrica, Mérida, Yucatán, Mexico (F. J. Cárdenas-Patrón)

Biochemistry Department, Laboratorios Nacionales de Fomento Industrial, Apartado Postal 41-537, Mexico 10, D. F. Mexico (O. Paredes-L., Chief)

Eugenio Palomo Y, Calle 82 #450-LL, Mérida, Yucatán, Mexico

Inter-American Institute of Agricultural Sciences, Londres 40-1, Mexico 6, D.F., Mexico (E. E. Fernandez)

Viveros "O N I L," Calle 66, N° 549, Mérida, Yucatán, Mexico (R. Sánchez-Espinosa)

R. S. Smith, Tanum-los-montes, Yucatán, Mexico

Viveros "O N I L," Calle 66, N° 549, Mérida, Yucatán, Mexico (R. Sánchez-Espinosa)

# CASSIA STURTII

*Cassia sturtii\**, a beautiful yellow-flowered shrub from the arid and semiarid regions of southern Australia, was introduced into Israel as an ornamental plant. However, recent research conducted at the Research and Development Authority of the Ben-Gurion University of the Negev in Beer-Sheva, has shown that it has great potential as a perennial fodder bush.

Under the conditions of the Negev desert, it has demonstrated better year-round palatability than any bush yet treated (*Atriplex* spp. [see page 122], *Kochia* spp., other *Cassia* spp., etc.). It has good grazing resistance and The leaves have a high protein content—about 12 percent—and annual dry-matter yields (in two grazing periods) of about 1,000 kg per ha in a 200 mm rainfall area.

The plant yields well in areas of 200-250 mm of winter rainfall, but also thrives in areas of higher rainfall. It will grow in a variety of soil types, including sandy and slightly alkaline soils, but does best in loamy soils.

Seedlings prepared in a nursery may be transplanted to the field 6-12 months after planting. If the soil is rain moistened at transplanting time, no irrigation is necessary. Under the conditions of the northern Negev plants grow quickly enough in loamy soil for grazing to start 1-1½ years after transplanting. Although seeds planted directly in the field grow successfully, overall growth is slower than when the transplanting method is used. Once established, the plants will voluntarily produce daughter plants in the neighboring area.

*\*Cassia sturtii* R. Br. Family: Leguminosae.

Ungrazed *Cassia sturtii.* (M. Forti)

## LIMITATIONS AND SPECIAL REQUIREMENTS

It has been claimed that sheep and cattle rarely graze *Cassia sturtii* in Australia, its homeland; this should serve as a warning to researchers who are considering introducing it into new areas. Only small-scale plantings should be attempted at first, and palatability trials should be instituted early.

The field trials in Israel included only a small percentage of *Cassia sturtii* within any grazing area. There has been no indication of any toxicity. However, with such a small proportion of the plant being consumed by livestock, toxicity may not have been evident.

Sheep graze the most accessible parts of *Cassia sturtii* first. Later (like this Awassi ram at Beer-Sheva, Israel) they return and strip the higher portions of the shrub. (M. Forti)

## RESEARCH NEEDS

Little or no selection has been done to improve *Cassia sturtii* potential as a forage. This is an immediate research need. Selection should be aimed at achieving higher yields and especially higher leaf-to-stem ratios. *Cassia sturtii* is one of a complex of closely related species, or subspecies, in inland Australia; much variability is available for selection and hybridization within this group.

More information on the plant's nutritive value is needed. Grazing trials are needed to determine effects on sheep and cattle growth and reproduction.

For a species introduced for exploitation under dry land conditions, climate, soil, and other environmental characteristics are of major importance (annual rainfall is only one factor affecting plant growth). Research is needed to test such factors before large-scale planting of *Cassia sturtii* is attempted in new locations.

Shrubs being farmed and tested as sources of livestock feed for desert regions. In these 3-year-old trials, 22 species, including *Cassia sturtii* and species of *Atriplex* (see page 122) are being compared for palatability, grazing resistance, regeneration ability, and yields. (M. Forti)

## Selected Readings

Cannon, W. A. 1921. *Plant Habits and Habitats in the Arid Portions of South Australia*. Carnegie Institution of Washington, Washington, D.C.

Forti, M. 1971. *Introduction of Fodder Shrubs and Their Evaluation for Use in Semi-arid Areas of the North-Western Negev*. Negev Institute for Arid Zone Research, Beer-Sheva, Israel.

Imperial Agricultural Bureaux. 1947. *The Use and Misuse of Shrubs and Trees as Fodder*. Joint Publication No. 10. Imperial Bureau of Pastures and Field Crops, Aberystwyth, Imperial Forestry Bureau, Oxford, Imperial Bureau of Animal Nutrition, Aberdeen.

Symon, D. E. 1966. A revision of the genus Cassia L. Caesalpiniaceae in Australia. *Transactions Royal Society of South Australia*. 90:73-151.

## Research Contacts and Germ Plasm Supply

C.S.I.R.O., Division of Plant Industry, P.O. Box 109, Canberra City, A.C.T., Australia (R. A. Perry)

Research and Development Authority, Ben-Gurion University of the Negev, P.O.B. 1025, Beer-Sheva, Israel (M. Forti)

Waite Institute of Agricultural Research, Adelaide, S. Australia (D. Symon)

# SALTBUSHES

Saltbushes of the genus *Atriplex*\* grow throughout the world. They are highly salt tolerant, and many are perennial shrubs that remain green all year. They make useful forage in arid zones of the world. For example, *Atriplex nummularia* grows well in deep soil with only 150-200 mm annual rainfall. They resist temperatures as low as $-10°$ to $-12°C$, withstand heavily textured soils, and tolerate salinity in soil or water.

Research indicates that the nutritive value of *Atriplex nummularia* and *Atriplex halimus* is high: both have a digestible protein content averaging 12 percent of the dry matter (about the same as that of alfalfa). With only 200 mm of rainfall these two species have produced 1,000-1,500 feed units per ha, which is about 8 to 10 times more than a good native pasture produces under the same conditions.† They have survived (but without reproducing) a 12-month period with only 50 mm rainfall.‡

---

\**Atriplex* spp. Commonly known as saltbushes. Family: Chenopodiaceae.

†Malet, 1969. Ziani, 1969. See Selected Readings.

‡Franclet and Le Houérou, 1971. See Selected Readings.

A plantation of *Atriplex* species established near Beer-Sheva, Israel, to provide forage for livestock. Rainfall here is about 200 mm annually. At the left is *Atriplex nummularia*; in the center (heavy with fruit), *Atriplex canescens*. Atriplexes can make areas productive that are otherwise useless and salt devastated: note the barrenness of the surrounding landscape. (M. Forti)

Awassi ram lamb grazing *Atriplex canescens* during the height of summer. This species has proved to be one of the most palatable in trials in Israel. (M. Forti)

*Atriplex nummularia*, although not considered a tropical plant, reaches into some tropical areas of Australia. Because of its importance as a forage plant for arid and semiarid areas, it should be among the first to be introduced into regions with similar climate. It is one of the most palatable of the atriplexes and is highly drought resistant. It has been introduced into Israel, South and North Africa, and into several South American countries for testing as a forage plant; yields in Israel have been high.

*Atriplex canescens* and *Atriplex canescens* ssp. *linearis* are North American species that grow in semiarid areas where spring and fall rainfall patterns are typical. These plants have as high a nutritive value as *Atriplex nummularia*. Palatability is similar to *Atriplex nummularia*; they are eaten by sheep and

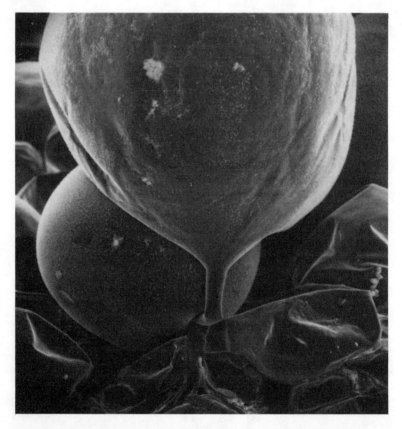

Atriplexes will grow in saline soils because they have a mechanism for "excreting" the salt that their roots absorb. Hairs on the leaf surfaces swell (as shown here) and accumulate salt; eventually they burst, scattering the salt over the outside surface of the leaf. (J. R. Goodin)

cattle. In Israel, sheep prefer them in the dry season. In a mixed system of shrubs and native annual vegetation, these and other newly introduced species have sustained sheep at the rate of 3 sheep per ha in an area of 250 mm annual (winter) rainfall.

In Israel and North Africa, *Atriplex halimus*, a Mediterranean species, has proved more hardy than either the *canescens* or the *nummularia*; however, it is· less palatable. It will grow in shallow soil and on slopes where the others cannot survive. Sheep and cattle show a preference for it during the rainy winter season and in early spring. It does well with a rainfall of 200 mm in winter, but should be planted or rotated with species more palatable in the dry summer and fall.

Atriplexes are salt tolerant. Laboratory experiments have demonstrated that *Atriplex halimus*, for instance, will grow adequately when irrigated with saline (nutritive) solution containing as much as 30,000 mg/liter of sodium chloride.* They excrete salt by forming small salt-filled bubbles (vesicles) on the leaf surfaces. When full, the vesicles burst, releasing the salt to the wind.

*Atriplex* cultivation is simple. Seedlings or cuttings are grown in a nursery for 3-6 months and then planted in the fields (1 m by 5 m apart) early in spring, preferably after rain. Normally atriplexes may be grazed when they are 1.5 m high, which is often in the second or third year. Native stands of *Atriplex halimus* yield about the same amount of browse and wood.

*Atriplex* is now cultivated in Tunisia as a fodder crop and several hundred additional hectares are planted every year.

Although only four species are mentioned here, other *Atriplex* species should be considered by researchers testing the use of atriplexes for arid-zone fodder.

## LIMITATIONS AND SPECIAL REQUIREMENTS

Some scientists have questioned the palatability of *Atriplex* species. However, numerous experiments and the experience of farmers show that *Atriplex* is accepted by livestock during the summer and fall (winter and early spring in western United States rangelands) when there is no green feed on the ranges.

Under saline conditions the leaves may have surface deposits of salt that may limit intake by livestock, especially when drinking water also has a high salt content or is in short supply. Low levels of oxalate have been found in *Atriplex*, but they are well below harmful amounts.

*Zid, 1970. See Selected Readings. For discussion of the importance of salt-tolerant plants to the development of arid lands see *More Water for Arid Lands*, BOSTID Report Number 14. Available without charge as noted on page 187.

The plants must first be nursery grown, which is a limitation because it increases investment costs.

In many areas *Atriplex* species attract rodents and other wild animals, which consume the seedlings before they have a chance to grow.


## RESEARCH NEEDS

There is urgent need for large-scale field trials with atriplexes. Management procedures, which could prove of vital importance, have not been investigated. Improved methods for sowing seeds directly in the field need to be developed.

Differences in salt resistance, drought resistance, salt content, leafiness, and palatability have been observed within populations of several species. Therefore, a wide research field is open in plant genetics, physiology, ecophysiology, and nutrition.

Selection and breeding could greatly improve yields, raise protein content, and reduce toxic substances. Geneticists should aim at selecting varieties that are shaped to make edible parts more available to sheep and cattle. Varieties that tolerate defoliation well and that have a vigorous pattern of regrowth after browsing are also needed.


### Selected Readings

Bonsma, H. C., and G. S. Maré, 1972. *Cactus and Oldman–Saltbush as Feed for Sheep.* Department of Agriculture and Forestry Bulletin No. 236. The Government Printer, Pretoria, South Africa.

Forti, M. 1971. *Introduction of Fodder Shrubs and Their Evaluation for Use in Semi-Arid Areas of the North-Western Negev.* Negev Institute for Arid Zone Research, Beer-Sheva, Israel.

Franclet, A., and H.N. Le Houérou. 1971. *Les Atriplex en Tunisie et en Afrique du Nord.* (English and French editions) Institute de Roboisement, Tunisie, FAO, Rome.

Imperial Agricultural Bureaux. 1947. *The Use and Misuse of Shrubs and Trees as Fodder.* Joint Publication No. 10. Imperial Bureau of Pastures and Field Crops, Aberystwyth; Imperial Forestry Bureau, Oxford; Imperial Bureau of Animal Nutrition, Aberdeen.

Jones, R. M. *et al* (Ed.) 1970. *The Biology of Atriplex. Studies of the Australian Arid Zone.* Commonwealth Scientific and Industrial Organization, Division of Plant Industry, Canberra, Australia.

Lachover, D., and N. Tadmore. 1965. Étude qualitative de l'*Atriplex halimus* comme plante fourragère poussant dans les conditions semi-arides d'Israel. *L'Agronomie Tropical.* 20:3, 13. Paris.

Le Houérou, H. N. 1974. *The Useful Shrubs of the Mediterranean Basin and the Arid Tropical Belt South of the Sahara.* Plant Division, FAO, Rome.

Le Houérou, H. N. 1970. North Africa: Past, Present, Future. In *Arid Lands in Transition*, Ed., Harold E. Dregne. pp. 227-78. American Association for the Advancement of Science, Washington, D.C.

Malet, P. H. 1969. *Premiers Resultats d'un Essai d'*Atriplex nummularia *sur sol Argilleux non Salé et sous Pluviosité Naturelle à Hendi Zitoun dans la Plaine de Kairouan*. Document Technical 133. Centre de Recherche de Genie Rural, Tunis, Tunisia.

Plummer, A. P., S. B. Monsen, and D. R. Christensen. 1966. *Fourwing Saltbush, a Shrub for Future Game Ranges*. Utah State Department of Fish and Game. Publication 66-4. Salt Lake City, Utah, USA.

Rodin, L., B. Vinogradov, H. Kalemov, Yu. Mirochnitchenko, N. Pelt, and Vo. Botschantzev. 1970. *Etude Géobotaniaue des Pâturages du Secteur Ouest du Departement de Médea (Algérie)*. Inst. Bot. Leningrad.

Sarson, M. 1970. *Résultats d'un Essai sur l'Alimentation du Mouton en Période de Disette Fourragère au Centre d'Ousseltia*. Technical Note 6. FAO, FSNU/Tun 17, Tunis, Tunisia.

Utah State University. 1972. *Wildland Shrubs—Their Biology and Utilization*. United States Department of Agriculture Forest Service General Technical Report INT-1. Intermountain Forest and Range Experiment Station, Ogden, Utah, USA.

Wilson, A. D. 1964. *The Sodium Intake of Sheep Fed with* Atriplex *sp. and* Kochia *sp.* Commonwealth Scientific and Industrial Organization, Division of Plant Industry, Melbourne, Australia.

Wilson, A. D. 1966. The value of *Atriplex* (saltbush) and *Kochia* (bluebush) species as food for sheep. *Australian Journal of Agricultural Research*. 17:147-53.

Ziani, P. 1969. *Exploitation des formations naturelles d'*Atriplex halimus. Commission pour l'Étude des *Atriplex*. Document No. 13, Institute National de Recherche Forestière de Tunisie. Tunis, Tunisia.

Zid, E. 1970. *Influence du Chlorure de Sodium sur la Croissance et la Nutrition Minerale d'*Atriplex halimus *var.* halimus. Centre de Recherche du Problem Zone Aride, Tunis, Tunisia.

## Research Contacts and Germ Plasm Supply

C.S.I.R.O., Division of Plant Industry, P.O. Box 109, Canberra, A.C.T., Australia

Department of Agriculture, Soils Division, Jarrah Road, South Perth, Western Australia (C. V. Malcolm)

F.A.O., Crop and Grassland Production Service, Via delle Terme di Caracalla, 00100, Rome, Italy (H. N. Le Houérou)

Grootfontein College of Agriculture, Middleburg, Cape Peninsula, South Africa (J. D. Aucamp)

Institut de Reboisement de Tunis, Tunis, Tunisia

Intermountain Forest and Range Experiment Station, Ephraim, Utah 84627, USA (A. P. Plummer)

Range Science Department, Utah State University, Logan, Utah 84321, USA (C. M. McKell)

Research and Development Authority, Ben-Gurion University, P.O.B. 1025, Beer-Sheva, Israel (M. Forti)

Society for Growing Australian Plants, 860 Henry Lawson Drive, Picnic Point, New South Wales, Australia.

# TAMARUGO

The tamarugo* grows in the forbidding Atacama Desert of northern Chile where a salt crust several feet thick covers the soil. Few useful plants can survive the extreme conditions of tamarugo's native habitat. In salt-devastated regions of suitable climate, tamarugo, an evergreen plant, could become a year-round fodder supply. Its pods, leaves, and seeds are nutritious and palatable, and it is used as fodder for sheep and goats.

The tamarugo is a sparsely branching, leguminous tree averaging 20-25 feet in height. Chile's nitrate industry used tamarugo timber extensively for fuel and construction in the early 1900s. A 300-ha plantation was established to replace almost extinct tamarugo woodlands. The first livestock experiments were conducted in 1962. As a result, a 40,000-ha tamarugo project is now under way; 25,000 hectares have already been planted.

To plant tamarugo, holes are cut through the salt crust. The seedling is planted well below the surface so it will reach the water table. This deep planting also protects the seedlings from desiccating winds. Seedlings have shown a 95-percent survival rate with just a single irrigation at transplanting. The 10-cm seedlings grow to 75 cm in their first year; within 5 years they are strong enough to withstand grazing at a rate equivalent to 1 ewe per ha. (After 25 years the sheep and goats are stocked at a rate of 10-20 animals per ha—the maximum that one hectare can sustain.) The trees are planted at 100-120 per ha.

Rain is scarce in the region (sometimes absent for as long as 7 years), but the trees receive moisture from a foggy drizzle and from the slightly brackish water table, which is 1-2 m below the surface and is fed by runoff from the nearby Andes.

Now growing through the salt, a woodland of tamarugo is supporting sheep at rates comparable to those of high-quality pasture elsewhere in the world. The sheep thrive, proving the palatability and nutritional value of tamarugo as forage. Since 1968 over 5,000 sheep have been maintained on tamarugo plantations. Angora goats and Karakul, Merino, Romney, and English Suffolk sheep are used for either wool production or meat. Meat from tamarugo-fed sheep has an acceptable flavor. Merinos have produced more than 4 kg of wool per animal.

A pilot introduction of 2,000 trees for goat fodder was established in highly saline soil on Las Palmas in the Canary Islands in 1973.

---

*Prosopis tamarugo* Phil. Family: Leguminosae.

Tamarugo's high-protein pods and leaves.  (M. Sarquis)

## LIMITATIONS AND SPECIAL REQUIREMENTS

Because little is known of the environmental consequences of introducing tamarugo to new regions, care should be taken that it does not become a pest. In extreme conditions similar to those in the Atacama Desert, it should be safe, but its aggressiveness in more hospitable regions is unknown.

Little is known of the economics of its plantation and use.

It is possible that the high-protein tamarugo diet may result in decreased fertility; rams should not be held permanently on the tamarugo plantations. Animals feeding on tamarugo require supplementary rations of cobalt, iron, magnesium, and vitamin A.

Since tamarugo is the only plant that does well in such harsh environments, a monoculture has been established. If disease or pests develop there will be few, if any, alternative sources of fodder for the livestock. Economic disaster might result.

A thorough pollination is essential because up to 70 percent of the fruit can be lost to insect pests. Throughout tamarugo plantations in Chile seedlings of the related algarrobo (*Prosopis chilensis* Stuntz) are occasionally introduced. The plants are not palatable to the sheep, but their earlier flowering provides food for the wild bees that pollinate the tamarugos.

Tamarugo pods need extensive leaching before they can be eaten by humans.

Sheep being fed among the tamarugo trees in Chile's Pampa del Tamarugal. This is one of the most salt-devastated areas in the world and rain is often absent for years on end. Nevertheless, sheep are raised on tamarugo at stocking rates approaching those obtainable on good pastures in temperate countries. (M. Sarquis)

## RESEARCH NEEDS

Pilot trials to raise tamarugo in Central America, northeast Brazil, the Middle East, and arid regions in Africa are recommended.

The tamarugo is outstanding in its ability to resist salinity stress. It could serve as an experimental plant for investigating the physiology of salt resistance. Such experimentation could also lead to means for raising tamarugo's productivity.

Selection and breeding methods to develop strains with higher yields of pods are badly needed; as yet no such research has been attempted.

Other salt-resistant species must be found to interplant with tamarugo. The economy of a plantation will then not be so dependent on the fate of a single species.

### Selected Readings

Elgueta Salinas, H., and S. Calderón Sánchez. 1971. Estudio del tamarugo como productor de alimento del ganado lanar en la Pampa del Tamarugal. (A study of tamarugo as producer of forage for sheep in the Pampa del Tamarugal.) *Informe Tecnológico.* 38:1-36. Instituto Forestal, Santiago, Chile.
Kirby, J. M. 1972. Chile's tamarugo project. *World Crops.* 24:296-8.

Programa Cooperativo FAO/BID. 1970. *Informe Sobre el Proyecto de Plantaciones de Tamarugo y explotacion ganadera en el Norte Grande, Chile.* Informe Numero 1/70 Ch. 1.b. Washington, D.C. 262 pp. Available from FAO Regional Office, Santiago, Chile.

Sudzuki, H. F. 1969. *Absorción Foliar de Humedad Atmosférica en Tamarugo (*Prosopis tamarugo *Phil.*) Boletín Técnico # 30, Universidad de Chile, Santiago. 23 pp. (Available from author, Escuela de Agronomía, Departamento Botánico, Campus Antumapu, Santiago, Chile.)

## Research Contacts and Germ Plasm Supply

Agricultural Planning Associates Limited, 85 New Cavendish Street, London W1M 7RA, England

Agricultural Research and Education Center, 18905 S.W. 280th Street, Homestead, Florida 33030, USA (S. Malo)

Depto. Agricultura y Agroindustrias, División de Desarrollo Ganadero, Corporación de Fomento de la Produccion, Santiago, Chile (Felix Susaeta Sáenz de San Pedro and Fernando Espinosa)

FAO Regional Office, Santiago, Chile (M. Habit)

Escuela de Agronomía, Departmento Botánico, Campus Antumapú, Santiago, Chile (F. Sudzuki)

Mario Sarquís, Isabel la Católica 4827 (Los Condes), Santiago, Chile.

Research and Development Authority, Ben-Gurion University of the Negev, P.O.B. 1025, Beer-Sheva, Israel (J. Schechter, M. Forti)

# VII OTHER USES

## BURITÍ PALM

The burití palm,* which grows by the millions throughout the Amazon basin, Venezuela, and the Guianas, has a remarkable range of uses. It is known as the tree of life because some Indian tribes depend on it for all aspects of their livelihood—food, drink, shelter, and clothing.

It may well be the most plentiful palm in South America, yet only minor attempts have been made at commercialization. Potential products from burití include oil and starch for food; wine; timber; cork; and industrial fiber for twine, sacking, nets, and hammocks. Feasibility studies of burití production and exploitation are recommended to researchers, private investors, and government agencies.

Burití palms grow mostly at low altitudes in groves near swamps and springs in damp soils that are useless for agriculture. Their presence often indicates the existence of water in dry country.

The burití have leaves 3 m long and reach heights of 25 m. The green, scaly fruit is roundish (about the size of an egg) and grows in bunches. After scraping, the fruit is soaked to soften the scales that cover the thin pulp. It has a pleasantly sweet, tangy taste and is reported to have as much vitamin C as citrus fruit. The fruit could be canned or candied and would probably enjoy wide distribution. The fruit pulp contains 8-9 percent edible oil, which contains 300 mg of beta-carotene per 100 g. This oil is said to produce more vitamin A than any other oil (and even more vitamin A than carrots and spinach).

The kernel inside the fruit is contained in a woody shell that cracks fairly easily. It yields almost 50 percent of a light-yellow oil that can be extracted with equipment already used for other oilseeds. Burití kernel oil appears to be similar in quality to more commonly used vegetable oils such as that from the African oil palm kernels.

Its shoots can be harvested for "hearts of palm" (see page 48). A sago-like starch, roasted by Amazon indians to make a bread, is obtained from the pith of its trunk. (Burití could also be a source for industrial starch.)

*Mauritia flexuosa L. Also known as Mauritia vinifera Mart., mirití, murití, moriche, muriche, ité, aetí, aguaje (Peru). Family: Palmae.

Wines are often made by the Indians from the fruit and from the sweet sap of the trunk and unopened flower cluster (inflorescence).

The hard outer part of the trunk yields light (but tough) buriti wood, which is used locally, much in the manner of balsa wood, to make rafts and floats. A cork-like material obtained from the leaf-stalk (petioles) has been used in the manufacture of sandals and for bottle-top linings.

Stripped from the outer skin of young leaves is a thread-like fiber that makes a strong twine. Though not fully tested, the fiber's wide use in Indian fishing nets, hammocks, mats, hats, and baskets indicates that it deserves further research.

## LIMITATIONS AND SPECIAL REQUIREMENTS

The buriti palm has seldom been grown outside its native habitat. Thus nothing is known of agronomic restrictions that will limit its use elsewhere. For example, its soil requirements and environmental tolerances are unknown. It may be limited to swampy locations, but it seems likely that if seedlings are germinated artificially the buriti can be grown to maturity in drier climates.

*Mauritia* fruit in the Colombian Amazonia. (R. E. Schultes)

*Mauritia* tree. (R. E. Schultes)

Blocks of paste made of the fruits of the Burití palm cooked with sugar, here being sold by street vendors in Ciudad Bolívar, Venezuela. (J. Morton)

## RESEARCH NEEDS

The agronomic requirements to produce burití in plantations are virtually unknown. Therefore, all factors affecting the feasibility of cultivation and harvesting should be explored before it can be mass cultivated outside its native South American soil. The economic aspects of harvesting and processing the wild stands also require extensive study.

Many opportunities exist for research and testing of burití products in food, fiber, and timber industries. Testing should involve methods for obtaining the raw products as well as their formulation and fabrication into marketable items. Obviously, this work will have to be done in the northern South American countries where the plant is now available in quantity.

Many of the points made here about burití also apply to some other neglected tropical palms. Others worthy of research are *Arenga pinnata* and *Nypa* spp. that are native to Southeast Asia. *Arenga pinnata*, for example, grows in drier soils than burití and it may prove superior to burití in regions where the waterlogged soils are taken up with rice cultivation.

## Selected Readings

Braun, A. 1968. Cultivated palms of Venezuela. *Principes*. 12:111-3.

Dugand, A. 1972. Las palmeras y el hombre. *Cespedesia*. I(1&2):31-97.

Corner, E. J. H. 1966. *The Natural History of Palms*. University of California Press, Berkeley and Los Angeles, USA.

Dodge, C. R. 1897. *Descriptive Catalogue of Useful Fiber Plants of the World #9*. U.S. Department of Agriculture, Office of Fiber Investigations, Washington, D.C.

Pérez-Arbeláez, E. 1956. *Plantas Utiles de Colombia*, Ed. 3. Roldan, Bogotá, Colombia.

Seemann, B. 1856. *Popular History of the Palms and Their Allies*. Lovell Reeve, London, England.

Sombroek, W. G. 1966. Mauritiaceae. *Amazon Soils: A Reconnaissance of the Soils of the Brazilian Amazon Region*. Wageningen. Cent. Landbouw Hoge School Publ. Veralagen Landbouwkundige onderz.

Suárez, M. 1966. Les utilisations du palmier "Moriche" (*Mauritia flexuosa* L. f.) chez les Warao du Delta de l'Orenoque, Territoire Delta. Amacuro, Venezuela. *Journal d'Agriculture Tropical et de Botanique Appliquée. 13(1/3):33-8.*

Wessels Boer, G. 1965. *The Indigenous Palms of Surinam*. E. J. Brill, Leiden, Netherlands.

## Research Contacts and Germ Plasm Supply

Bailey Hortarium, Cornell University, Ithaca, New York 14850, USA (H. E. Moore)

Botanical Garden, Universidad Central de Venezuela, Caracas, Venezuela (A. Braun)

CEPLAC, Itabuna, Bahia, Brazil (P. de T. Alvin)

Consejo de Bienestar Rural, Apartado 61.407, Caracas, 106, Venezuela (R. Araque)

Department of Botany, Smithsonian Institution, Washington, D.C. 20560, USA (R. W. Read)

Fairchild Tropical Garden, 13601 Old Cutler Road, Miami, Florida 33158, USA (J. Popenoe)

Morton Collectanea, University of Miami, P.O. Box 248204, Coral Gables, Florida 37724, USA (J. F. Morton)

# CALATHEA LUTEA

*Calathea lutea** is a tall, large-leafed herb that grows in semi-inundated or upland areas and along river banks in South and Central America. The coating on its leaves is a potential source of commercial wax that is similar to, and can be used for the same purposes as, carnauba, the best wax known. Extract-

*Calathea lutea* (Aublet) Schultes. Also known as cauassú, casupo, hoja blanca, and bijao. Family: Marantaceae.

*Calathea lutea* growing in waterlogged soil in the Amazon Basin.  (J. M. Idrobo)

ing wax from *Calathea lutea* could be developed into a productive cottage industry, particularly suited to isolated regions. Because the chemical structure of such fine waxes is difficult to synthesize industrially, natural products have an edge over synthetics.* Furthermore, carnauba wax is in great demand, and its price is rising because of the expense and difficulty of obtaining it from the Brazilian palm *Copernicia cerifera.*

*Calathea lutea* grows naturally in dense stands along Amazon River banks; it is readily accessible and its harvested leaves can be easily transported. But it is also a potential new plantation crop for regions outside its native habitat. It should be test planted along river banks elsewhere in the wet tropics (in such places as Southeast Asia, Papua New Guinea, Central and West Africa, and the Guianas), especially in newly logged or semi-inundated areas. This species is one of the first secondary-growth species to colonize newly disturbed areas.

*See also Candelilla page 141 and Jojoba page 105.

The wax (known as cauassú wax) occurs as a thin layer on the underside of the leaf. The rapidly growing leaves mature in 9 months and have an average yield of 0.7 g wax.* This wax can be removed easily, without machinery, but contains a resin which, for some end uses, must be removed by solvent extraction.

*Calathea lutea* is easily propagated from seed or from pieces of rhizome by simply pushing them into the soil or mud and leaving them to sprout. As many as 75,000 plants can grow on one hectare. One harvest is possible the first year; thereafter two harvests per year result in an annual yield of 800 kg of crude wax per ha.

## LIMITATIONS AND SPECIAL REQUIREMENTS

The major problem is the difficulty of extracting the wax from the leaves.

## RESEARCH NEEDS

Chemists and engineers are needed to develop more efficient techniques for separating the wax from the leaf. After the *Calathea lutea* leaves are dried, the wax often flakes off easily, which may become an important processing consideration.

There seems to be an immediate market for cauassú wax. In the Amazon regions, where the plant now grows in dense stands, small industries could be set up immediately, perhaps in the communities developing along the Trans-Amazon Highway.

The entire Marantaceae family should be examined for species with higher wax yields than *Calathea lutea*.

Other waxy species of Marantaceae that deserve particular attention are *Ischnosiphon leucophaeus* (P. & E.) Koern, and *Monotagma rhodantha* Maguire & Wurdack. However, these are more restricted in distribution than *Calathea lutea*; they are smaller plants, and not so good at colonizing new areas. Thus, for cultivation they may require more attention.

A program is needed for selecting and breeding natural strains that have high wax yield.

A number of *Calathea* species have edible roots. Some examples are *Calathea allouia*, *Calathea latifolia*, and *Calathea macrosepala*. Their potential to become important food crops has not been systematically evaluated. Research could prove rewarding.

---

*One member of the panel (Mors) has not been able to duplicate the yield of 0.7 g wax from a leaf 20 × 50 cm that is reported in the literature.

## Selected Readings

Acosta-Solís, M. 1973. Producción de céras vegetales. *La Hacienda.* 68(10):20-2.
Anonymous 1944. Lower-Amazon plant has possible commercial value. *Agriculture in the Americas.* 4(2):37.
Mors, W. B., and C. T. Rizzini. 1966. *Useful Plants of Brazil.* Holden-Day, Inc., San Francisco.
Standley, P. C., and J. A. Steyermark. 1952. *Flora of Guatemala.* 24(3):212-3. Field Museum of Natural History, Chicago, Illinois, USA.
Wastler, T. A., P. M. Daugherty, and H. H. Sineath. 1953. Industrial raw material of plant origin. *II Recent Developments in Vegetable Waxes, Gums, and Resins.* Bulletin 15. p. 7. Engineering Experiment Station, Georgia Institute of Technology, Atlanta, Georgia, USA.

## Research Contacts and Germ Plasm Supply

Botanical Museum, Harvard University, Oxford Street, Cambridge, Massachusetts 02138, USA (R. E. Schultes)
Centro de Recursos Naturáis da Amazônia, Belém, Pará, Brazil (J. Pires)
Department of Botany, Smithsonian Institution, Washington, D.C. 20560, USA (E. S. Ayensu)
Germ plasm could be readily collected in the vicinity of Leticia, Colombia.

The wax-covered leaf of *Calathea lutea.* (J. M. Idrobo)

# CANDELILLA

The leafless stems of the North American desert shrub candelilla* exude a white wax that has valuable industrial potential. Although wild stands are harvested occasionally, no effort has been made to develop candelilla into a crop. Research could adapt the plant to cultivation, reduce harvesting costs, and improve the wax-extraction process. With these improvements candelilla could become an important source for bringing foreign currency to arid developing nations.

Synthetic waxes (largely based on petroleum) have not replaced natural waxes in the marketplace. A continuing market for natural waxes is foreseen, especially if production could be modernized. The candelilla plant appears adaptable to mechanized cultivation. Modern extraction methods can be used, resulting in a cheaper and superior wax. The production of carnauba wax, candelilla's major competitor, requires much hand labor and cannot be easily mechanized. As labor costs increase, and carnauba becomes more expensive, candelilla wax might replace carnauba.†

Candelilla wax is an amorphous solid, yellowish brown in color, that is used as a substitute for beeswax and carnauba. When refined, it is used as a hardener for soft waxes (e.g. paraffin wax) in candles, polishes, chewing gum, leather goods, varnishes and lacquers, sealing waxes, paper sizing, dental molds, and electrical insulating materials.

Abundant in deserts from the Big Bend area of Texas and southern New Mexico to the Coahuilan desert in Mexico, candelilla requires only 100-500 mm of annual rainfall. It grows best on rocky, sandy slopes, in soil that is well drained and poor in humus. The waxy coat on stems and leaves is reported to be thicker in drier months and drier areas. Candelilla makes good forage for goats and rabbits and does not seem highly susceptible to diseases or pests. The plants can be easily propagated from cuttings or from divisions placed in moist sand. They require from 2-5 years to produce wax in quantities sufficient for commercial use. Candelilla wax can be produced year-round, but most is now harvested during the winter, when migrant workers are available. Sometimes, plants are harvested and stacked for later wax extraction.

The waxy cover separates when the leaves and stems are boiled in water or the wax may be extracted with solvent. Only 2 percent of a plant's weight is removed as wax under primitive field conditions, but yields of 3-5 percent

---

*Euphorbia antisyphilitica* Zucc. [*Euphorbia cerifera* Alcocer]. Family: Euphorbiaceae.
†For other competitors discussed in this report, see Jojoba page 105 and *Calathea lutea* page 137.

The candelilla plant. (W. H. Earle)

have been achieved in laboratory tests. The primitive methods now in use contaminate the wax with colored impurities.

Candelilla wax is marketed in the United States at about $1.50 per kg. In the past, the United States imported nearly 5 million kg per year; almost half was used in coatings and polishes and one-third for chewing gum.


## LIMITATIONS AND SPECIAL REQUIREMENTS

Attempts to cultivate candelilla in Haiti, Cuba, the Dominican Republic, and other regions outside its native habitat have not been successful.

Mechanized harvesting of candelilla may prove destructive to the plants; mowing off the shoots causes the plants to bleed. Severe frosts will kill the plant back to its roots.

Candelilla's arid habitat. Harvested plants in background. (W. H. Hodge)

Candelilla wax contains resin. Resin is a disadvantage in some products, but its tackiness is an asset in nonslip floor waxes.

The Mexican Government subsidizes the candelilla industry to support inhabitants of remote areas. The stems are gathered from native stands scattered over a large area and are then transported by burros to processing stations. The primitive transportation method and extraction process make the product expensive and the subsidy necessary. Candelilla will not expand or reach its potential as a crop until it is domesticated.

## RESEARCH NEEDS

Agronomic and engineering research is necessary before candelilla can be successfully cultivated and processed. Research and development programs should concentrate on:
* Developing plantation technology and agronomy;
* Developing higher-yielding varieties;
* Improving harvest techniques;
* Improving the extraction process to increase the quality of the wax produced;

Extracting candelilla wax in northern Mexico.  (W. H. Hodge)

• Developing new uses and markets for the wax; and
• Developing new uses and markets for the fibrous vegetable residue from
the wax extraction.

## Selected Readings

Daugherty, P. M., H. H. Sineath, and T. A. Wastler. 1953. A survey of candelilla and
candelilla wax. In *Industrial Raw Materials of Plant Origin. III.* Georgia State
Engineering Experiment Station Bulletin 15(12). Georgia Institute of Technology,
Atlanta, Georgia.
Hodge, W. H., and H. H. Sineath. 1956. The Mexican candelilla plant and its wax.
*Economic Botany.* 10(2):134-54.
Martínez, M. 1959. *Plantas Utiles de la Flora Mexicana.* Ediciones Botas, Mexico.

## Research Contacts and Germ Plasm Supply

Escuela Superior de Agropecuaria, Antonio Narro, Saltillo Coahuila, Mexico.

# GUAR

Guar* is a leguminous herb resembling the soybean plant to which it is related. With sufficient research support it could become a top-ranking agricultural crop in many tropical and subtropical countries of the world.

Its potential lies in the gum in its seeds. Guar gum has 5-8 times the thickening power of starch. It is used as a filter aid in the mining industry; as a thickener in cosmetics, hand lotions, and creams; and as a strengthening agent in paper. It is also used to thicken and stabilize salad dressings, bakery products, and ice cream. The demand for this valuable gum in industry is constantly increasing.

The gum is extracted from the seed's endosperm. It is primarily a galactomannan polysaccharide, and has high viscosity at low concentrations and over a wide range of acidities. Some 25,000 tons are already produced annually in the United States, but the demand exceeds the supply. One half goes to the paper industry; one third to the making of ice cream, desserts, cheese preparations, reconstituted tobacco, cosmetics, and pharmaceuticals; and the rest to the oil industry where it is used to stabilize drilling muds.

Guar also holds great promise for supplying protein required in the human diet. Guar seed contains about 34 percent protein, 23 percent gum, and 40 percent oil. It has been grown for food in India since ancient times. Young pods are eaten like stringbeans, or they may be dried, salted, or fried in oil.

The cake that remains after removing the gum is also rich in protein; both the seed and cake contain a balance of amino acids that complements the amino acid deficiencies in corn protein, wheat protein, and rice protein. Bread has been enriched with 8 percent guar protein in experiments without adversely affecting flavor. But, regrettably, guar protein is not used for human consumption. Guar seedcake (mixed with the hulls) is used only as cattle feed.

The plant grows best in semiarid areas and tolerates moderate salinity. It is robust, bushy, and normally grows 1-2 m tall. The crop matures within 3-5 months after planting. On the main stem and branches it bears leathery pods containing up to 10 seeds.

An annual crop, it is easily planted, cultivated, and harvested by existing agricultural machinery. Guar seeds do not shatter; an ordinary grain combine or soybean harvester can be used.

The guar plant is drought tolerant, performing well in areas having 400-900 mm of rainfall. When moisture is short, growth stops until moisture again becomes available.

*Cyanopsis tetragonoloba* (L.) Taub. Also known as *C. psoralioides* DC., cluster bean. Family: Leguminosae.

Guar grows well in a variety of soils and thrives in alluvial and sandy loam with well-drained subsoil. It is grown on rotation for the benefit of succeeding crops; it rotates well with cotton, sorghum, corn, and vegetables.

In some regions of the world guar is grazed, usually after frost (to reduce bloat problems), and makes good forage. Rain-fed guar will yield from 18,000-24,000 kg of green fodder and 900 kg of seed per ha. Yields may double with irrigation, with seed yield as high as 1,900 kg/ha.

Guar. (U. S. Department of Agriculture)

Guar grown between corn as a soil-improving crop. A nitrogen-fixing legume, guar provides the soil with nitrogenous materials similar to the main ingredients in fertilizer; at the same time, guar seeds can be harvested for the valuable gum they contain. (U. S. Department of Agriculture)

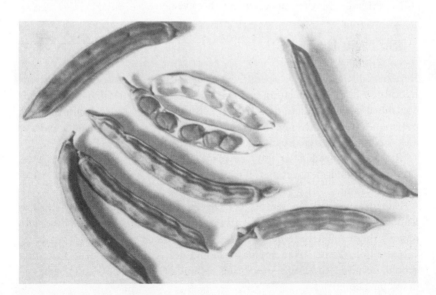

Guar pods and seeds. (R. Whistler)

At present it is grown mainly in Pakistan, India, and the United States, with some production in Australia, Brazil, and South Africa. Current prices range from $1.15 to $1.50 per kg of gum and approximately $2.50 per kg for edible grades.

## LIMITATIONS AND SPECIAL REQUIREMENTS

Mature guar seeds contain antitrypsin and hemolytic factors (just as soybeans do) that may adversely affect digestion and health.

Weeds can have a deleterious effect on guar seed yields, especially in fields infested with Johnson grass. Early preparation of the field and mechanical cultivation during the growing period are necessary. Guar is frost sensitive and susceptible to viral, fungal, and bacterial diseases, but is not affected by nematodes. Guar buds are attacked by midges, which often reduce yield.

The plant has photoperiod restrictions and may not grow well at all latitudes, but presumably (as with soybeans) this can be overcome by selecting appropriate varieties.

After pods mature, rain causes guar seed to blacken, adversely affecting gum quality. In areas with high rainfall and humidity guar is best grown as a soil-improvement crop rather than for its seeds.

Unless diluted, guar products may not become widespread food ingredients because the flour has an unusual flavor. Heat treatment will remove it, but this adds an often unacceptable inconvenience.

## RESEARCH NEEDS

Relatively little genetic selection has yet been done. The difficulty of making hybrids by hand emasculation makes it imperative that techniques for making controlled crossbreeding be developed before any guar varietal improvement program can proceed. Great potential exists for improving yield and for adapting the plant to a broader range of climates.

Research is needed to test the plant's susceptibility to insects, viruses, *Cecidomyia* midges, bacterial blight, and *Alternaria* fungi and to select resistant strains.

Human antinutrition factors present in the beans need study. If it is demonstrated that they adversely affect guar protein utilization, methods to remove them will have to be developed. The methods developed for removing antinutrition factors from soybeans should provide good models. Attention should be given to simple processing techniques suitable for rural areas in developing countries.

An important research goal is genetic selection and improvement of rapidly maturing varieties—essential for dry-land farming and multiple cropping.

## Selected Readings

Allen, G. H. 1964. Guar shows promise. *Queensland Agriculture Journal*. 90(4):224-7.

Hodges, R. J. *et al*. 1970. Keys to profitable guar production. *Fact Sheet*. L-907:1-4. Texas A & M University, Agricultural Extension Service, College Station, Texas.

Hymowitz, T., and R. S. Matlock. 1964. Guar: Seed, plant and population studies. *Oklahoma Agricultural Experimental Station Technical Bulletin*. 108:1-35. Stillwater, Oklahoma, USA.

Islam Shaw, S. S., M. B. Sial, and B. H. Schneider. 1966. The digestibility of guar meal. *Agriculture Pakistan*. 17(1):35-9.

Misra, D. K., S. Bham, and R. Prasad. 1968. Guar—a multipurpose summer legume. *Allahabad Farmer*. 42(4):299.

Oke, O. L. 1967. Nitrogen fixing capacity of guar bean. *Tropical Science*. 9(3):144-7.

Poats, F. J. 1960. Guar, a summer row crop for the southwest. *Economic Botany*. 14(3):241-6.

Whistler, R., and T. Hymowitz. (in Press) *Guar: A Food and Industrial Crop*. American Association of Cereal Chemists, 3340 Pilot Knob Road, St. Paul, Minnesota, USA.

## Research Contacts and Germ Plasm Supply

Agricultural Research Center, U.S. Department of Agriculture, Beltsville, Maryland 20705, USA (H. Hyland)

Agricultural Research Service, U.S. Department of Agriculture, Texas A & M Research and Extension Center, Vernon, Texas 76384, USA (R. Stafford)

Department of Agronomy, Oklahoma State University, Stillwater, Oklahoma 74074, USA (J. Kirby)

Department of Agronomy, University of Illinois, Urbana, Illinois 61801, USA (T. Hymowitz)

Department of Biochemistry, Purdue University, Lafayette, Indiana 47907, USA (R. Whistler)

Government Agriculture Research Farm, Durgapura, Jaipur-302004, Rajasthan, India (U. Menon and M. M. Dube)

Plant Introduction Division, Indian Agricultural Research Institute, New Delhi, India (Director)

# GUAYULE

The guayule*† shrub grows in desert regions of north central Mexico and the southwestern United States. All parts of the shrub contain a rubber that, when purified, is virtually indistinguishable from natural rubber from *Hevea* trees. A potential source of rubber for arid lands, it grows in poor desert soils in otherwise unused marginal areas.

*Parthenium argentatum* Gray. Family: Compositae

†A detailed report on guayule and its modern promise is being prepared by the National Academy of Sciences. Copies may be obtained from the address listed on page 188.

The possibility that this plant could become a source of natural rubber is especially important at this time. *Hevea* rubber still supplies one-third of the world's market and is widely used in such major products as automobile tires. The rest of the rubber goods currently produced are made from synthetic elastomers. These are superior to natural rubber for some uses, but inferior for many. A more important drawback is that elastomers are based on petroleum, an increasingly costly resource. This gives new impetus to attempts to overcome the technical problems that, so far, have made guayule only a minor rubber source.

At the turn of the century, German interests built several guayule rubber extraction plants in Mexico. Much research and development on the plant was conducted in the United States during the early 1940s, and about 1.3 million kg were produced during World War II. High-yielding strains and improved methods for extracting the rubber were developed. But after the war when rubber from Asian *Hevea* trees again became available, the methods already developed were not continued and the research was abandoned.

The rubber is contained within cells throughout the entire plant, but the roots and stems are particularly rich. To obtain the rubber, the whole plant is harvested. It is then sliced into small fragments, the tissues are macerated, and the lighter rubber is floated away from the vegetable residue. Yields of up to 12 percent (dry weight) have been obtained from wild plants and over 20 percent from improved varieties. Guayule can be harvested and processed with equipment (slightly modified) already developed for other crops.

Guayule shrubs may live for as long as 50 years. They represent a living stockpile of rubber.

Guayule is apomictic: the flowers do not require pollination to set seed. The varietal characteristics can be perpetuated through the seeds, which greatly simplifies replication of varieties and facilitates plantation culture.

## LIMITATIONS AND SPECIAL REQUIREMENTS

In the 1940s and 1950s seeds were furnished to more than 30 countries (Spain and Turkey embarked on large-scale production programs) but there is neither commercial production nor use of the wild plant today.

Because of inadequate processing technology, guayule rubber was of poor quality before and during World War II. Residual resin impurities posed the major difficulty.

A pilot-plant operation to process natural stands of guayule was recently established in Mexico. Although last reports still noted some difficulty in producing a pure rubber, the most recent results are encouraging and commercial production is expected within a few years.

Four-year-old guayule shrub ready for harvest. As much as 20 percent of the plant is rubber. (U. S. Department of Agriculture)

## RESEARCH NEEDS

The agricultural research conducted during World War II on the domestication of guayule needs to be reviewed. Field trials should be renewed, using the higher-yielding strains that were developed at that time.

Research should emphasize extraction processes (such as solvent extraction) that efficiently and economically remove resins and leave a pure latex. Some extraction methods have been developed, but they must be fully tested before real progress can be made.

### Selected Readings

Crocker, R. L., and H. C. Trumble. 1945. *Investigations of Guayule* (Parthenium argentatum *Gray) in South Australia*. Bulletin 192. Council of Science and Industrial Research, Melbourne, Australia.

Guayule under cultivation, Salinas, California (circa 1949). (U.S. Department of Agriculture)

In the early days of a major research program to develop guayule, the U.S. Secretary of Commerce, Jesse Jones, was presented (January 14, 1942) with the first automobile tire made entirely of rubber from guayule (right). (Wide World Photos)

Hammond, B. L., and L. G. Polhamus. 1965. *Research on Guayule* (Parthenium argentatum): *1942-1959*. Technical Bulletin 1327. U.S. Department of Agriculture, Agricultural Research Service, Washington, D.C.

Lloyd, F. E. 1911. *Guayule* (Parthenium argentatum *Gray*), *a Rubber Plant of the Chihuahuan Desert.* Publication 139. Carnegie Institution, Washington, D.C., USA.

Shapter, R. E. 1952. *Rubber Accumulation in Guayule* (Parthenium argentatum *Gray*) *in South Australia.* Bulletin 270. Commonwealth Scientific and Industrial Research Organization, Melbourne, Australia.

Taylor, K. W. 1951. Guayule—an American source of rubber. *Economic Botany.* 5(3):255-73.

## Research Contacts and Germ Plasm Supply

Centro de Investigaciones en Química Aplicada, Aldama Ote. No. 371, Saltillo, Coahuila, Mexico (E. Campos, Director)

College of Agriculture, University of Arizona, Tucson, Arizona 85721, USA (R. E. Dennis)

Comisión Nacional de las Zonas Aridas, Tonala No. 30, Mexico 7, D. F. (Sen. B. Fernández Aguirre, Director General; B. Canales L.; and M. Rodríguez)

Gray Herbarium, Harvard University, Cambridge, Massachusetts 02138, USA (R. Rollins)

Research and Development Authority, Ben-Gurion University of the Negev, P.O.B. 1025, Beer-Sheva, Israel (M. Forti)

U.S. Department of Agriculture, Germ Plasm Resources Laboratory, Beltsville, Maryland 20705, USA (H. Hyland)

Universidad Autónoma Agraria "Antonio Narro," Saltillo, Coahuila, Mexico (J. G. Medina T., Vice-rector de Investigaciones)

Universidad Técnica de Torreón, Torreón, Mexico

Pacific Rubber Growers, 831 Milan Ave., South Pasadena, California 91030, USA (H. Anderson)

# PASPALUM VAGINATUM

Silt grass,* a salt-tolerant rhizomatous grass, is recommended for revegetating salt-affected areas. It is also a good sand-binding plant, thriving in dry, sandy, beach soils, with vigorous runners that assist in stabilizing the soil. Silt grass is especially suited to soil subject to occasional inundation by seawater or to permanent brackish water seepage. It will grow with nonsaline water and

*Paspalum vaginatum* Swartz. Also known as seashore paspalum, sheathed paspalum, salt water couch, etc. Family: Gramineae.

Abnormally high fall tides flooded the water edge of King's Bay golf course daily for one month. Bermuda grass is dead and brown. Border of healthy green *Paspalum vaginatum* stands out in contrast. (J. Morton)

with water up to a salinity of at least 10,000 ppm; it may tolerate higher water salinities in soil that permits periodic leaching of the salts.* It is much more salt tolerant than common lawn grasses (e.g., couch and buffalo grass) and has a higher salt tolerance than even coastal Bermuda grass.

Silt grass appears to be a satisfactory forage grass. Once established, it withstands grazing well (even by sheep) and is valuable green feed during hot months. It also makes fine-textured lawns. The plant is easily propagated; new areas may be started by small sods (13-20 square cms) or by runners either placed on the surface or partially buried. Under favorable conditions, the runners from one small sod may, after one growing season, cover an area up to 1 m diameter. Little fertilizer is needed; under saline conditions the grass does not respond well to nitrogen and phosphorus. The use of fertilizer may be warranted only in low-salinity seepage areas.

Though it grows wild on seacoasts of both hemispheres from Australia to southern Spain and from Argentina and Chile to Baja California and North

*For a discussion of the importance of salt-tolerant plants see *More Water for Arid Lands*, a companion to this report. Ordering information is given on page 187.

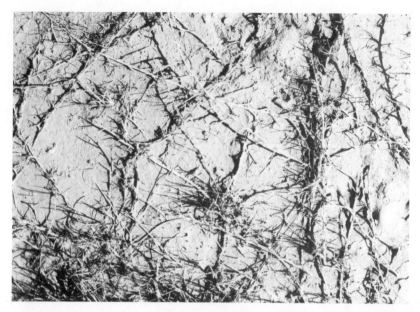

*Paspalum vaginatum,* here growing in saline soil in Australia, is good for revegetating salt-devastated regions and for erosion control. (G. R. MacPhie)

*Paspalum vaginatum* in seed. Sea Island, Georgia. (J. Morton)

Carolina, *Paspalum vaginatum* has been domesticated only in Australia, Florida, and the Netherlands Antilles. Experiments in domestication are now under way in Venezuela.

## LIMITATIONS AND SPECIAL REQUIREMENTS

It has been found that South American strains must have an adequate supply of summer moisture. If not, the plant, which is dormant in winter in subtemperate (not tropical) climates, will grow little during summer and its spread will be restricted.

In low-salinity soils silt grass is attacked by nematodes, but this is unlikely to occur in the saline soil where this grass is most useful. It is also sensitive to herbicides. It is not recommended for hay.

Because it produces only a small yield of viable seed, commercial supplies of propagation material are inadequate to meet current demands.

## RESEARCH NEEDS

Crop and sod nurseries should be established in tropical countries to furnish the grass for private and commercial use. The grass is already growing prolifically in subtemperate to tropical coastal regions around the world. Sod or runners should be distributed to tropical coastal areas for forage use and landscaping.

Insufficient information is available on the nutritional value of silt grass as a forage crop. Research should be directed towards breeding and selecting improved (but still salt-tolerant) strains for forage.

Developing a strain that produces large quantities of viable seed would reduce establishment costs and would hasten the plant's more widespread use. Development of a strain with greater winter hardiness would be useful in subtemperate, saline areas.

### Selected Readings

MacPhie, G. R. 1973. Three successful salt-tolerant plants. *Journal of Agriculture, South Australia*. 76(1):5-8.

Malcolm, C. V. and I. A. F. Laing. 1969. *Paspalum vaginatum*—for salty seepages and lawns. *Journal of Agriculture, Western Australia*. 10(11):474-5.

Morton, J. F. 1973. Salt-tolerant silt grass (*Paspalum vaginatum* Sw.). *Proceedings of Florida State Horticultural Society*. 86:482-90.

## Research Contacts and Germ Plasm Supply

Boca Patrick Estates, Curaçao, Netherlands Antilles (H. Riese, Manager)
Department of Agriculture, Jarrah Road, South Perth 6151, Australia. (C. V. Malcolm)
Golf Course Architect, King's Bay Yacht and Country Club, Miami, Florida 33158, USA
(C. Mahannah)
Sea Island Golf Club, Sea Island, Georgia 31561, USA (T. M. Baumgardner)
Technical Officer, Soils, Department of Agriculture, Jamestown, South Australia (G. R.
MacPhie)

# RAMIE

An important crop in China and Japan for many centuries, ramie* is one of the oldest fibers known. Native to East Asia, it will also grow in many regions with climates ranging from tropical to temperate.

A tall, slender herb, ramie has stems 3 m or higher. The bast layer contains fibers that are superior to other natural fibers in length and strength. Ramie has great potential to become an important plantation industry and cash crop for many tropical and subtropical locations. However, this potential is unrealized because of the technical problem involved in separating the fiber from green vegetable matter, and because of the tenacious gum coating. The problem exists even though the British Government offered a prize for its solution more than a hundred years ago.

Today's fiber market demands that any new vegetable fiber possess extraordinary qualities. Beyond question, ramie has them. If techniques can be developed for removing the gum without weakening the fiber, many markets for ramie will open up. The argument for further research and development is strengthened by the rising costs of petroleum-based synthetic fibers.

Ramie fibers are long (20-40 cm), durable, and lustrous. They have eight times the tensile strength of cotton and seven times that of silk. For some unusual reason the strength increases (about 60 percent) when wet. They are more resistant to chemicals and decay than most other vegetable fibers.

Ramie can be used for clothing, fabrics, upholstery, string, and paper. Blended with wool (with as little as 25 percent ramie) stretch and shrink are prevented and wear is greatly improved. A 50/50 mixture with wool is

*Boehmeria nivea (L.) Gaud. Also known as China grass, ramio, or rhea, var. tenacissima. Family: Urticaceae.

Flowering ramie. The top portion of the ramie plant makes nutritious and palatable fodder for livestock. (M. Petruszka)

reputed to double the wear of carpets. Ramie fabrics have three times the durability of cotton. They also "breathe" (i.e., they absorb and liberate moisture quickly).

A perennial plant, ramie is propagated by division of the clumps; planting seeds or cuttings is also acceptable. The plant is relatively pest free. Little cultivation is needed except to inhibit weeds until the crop itself shades them out. When properly cared for, a single planting has been known to yield productively for 10 years or more. A crop can be harvested six times a year under favorable climatic and soil conditions.

In recent years the protein content of ramie leaves have attracted some attention. Similar in quality to alfalfa, the leaves and tops have much potential as forage for livestock and poultry. Results from experimental plots suggest that it is possible to obtain 20 tons of leaves (20 percent protein) in addition to the normal yield of fiber. Thus, ramie has a promising future as a dual-purpose crop that produces forage and fiber at the same time.

Ramie is processed into fiber in three steps—harvesting, decorticating, and degumming. At harvest the tops and leaves of the plant are removed and can provide forage. Decorticating (the fiber bundles are separated from the stem and scraped to remove most of the gum) gives crude fiber. Decorticated fiber is hung over poles to dry and bleach in the wind and sun. Yields of as much as 1,400 kg of fiber per hectare may result from well-established ramie fields. However, almost half the yield is lost in the third step—degumming. Many degumming methods have been devised, but all are harsh and weaken the fiber because of the gum's tenacity and inertness.

In spite of its excellent properties, the fiber is not utilized on any large scale outside East Asia. The principal producing countries are China (especially the middle Yangtze and southern regions), the Philippines, Japan, Indonesia, Malaysia, India, and Brazil. It is probable that at least 100,000 tons of ramie fiber are produced annually in China.

## LIMITATIONS AND SPECIAL REQUIREMENTS

The extraction of the fiber presents serious difficulty. Unlike other stem fibers (such as jute, flax, and hemp) ramie fiber cannot be extracted satisfactorily by the usual retting (bacterial) methods because of the gum and a different bast structure. Extraction of the fiber by present methods involves tedious manual labor.

Before the fiber can be spun, the gum must be removed. All current methods demand considerable experience and technique. Removing the gum from ramie without weakening the fibers is the major obstacle to its widespread use.

Two-month-old ramie ready for harvest. The fiber is contained within the stems. (M. Petruszka)

In industrialized regions, ramie spinning is commonly done on machinery developed for silk, cotton, or wool—often with less than satisfactory results. Ramie fibers differ from other bast fibers—flax, hemp, and jute—in that they cannot be spun as fiber bundles. The long ramie fibers have a larger diameter than the other vegetable fibers, which makes them more rigid.

The ramie plant will grow under a variety of climatic conditions. However, profitable exploitation requires harvesting as many cuttings per year as possible. Multiple harvests are possible only with steady, high temperatures, a humid atmosphere, and a well-distributed annual rainfall of not less than 1,125 mm. Irrigation may be needed during prolonged dry periods. With repeated cutting, heavy fertilization is usually necessary to maintain the crop's vigor.

## RESEARCH NEEDS

The most urgent research and development need is to explore more efficient, cheaper ways to degum without weakening the fiber. This offers challenges to organic chemists to identify the gum's structure and to find solvents and techniques for dissolving it. It also challenges microbiologists to determine why ramie fiber (unlike jute and kenaf) cannot be separated by bacterial action. Microbiologists must also find and raise special microorganisms that will clean vegetable matter and gum from ramie fibers (perhaps under industrial conditions).

Ramie plants just 29 days old. Santiago de las Vegas, Cuba. (U.S. Department of Agriculture)

With current methods, decortication is best done with freshly cut stems. Therefore, decorticators suitable for medium- or small-scale operations in the field are needed.

It has been suggested that a mechanical harvester be invented to top the plant, recover the forage for livestock and poultry, harvest and decorticate the stems, and collect the decorticating waste for use as paper pulp—all in a single operation.

## Selected Readings

Allison, R. V. 1951. Ramie, long-, strong-fibered marvel, comes to stay. *Florida Grower*. 59(10):22-4.

Allison, R. V., and J. W. Randolph. 1954. Progress in the harvesting and processing of ramie and kenaf. *Proceedings of the Soil Science Society of Florida*. 14:190-201.

Blasco, M., and N. Bohorquez-A. 1967. Algunas características químicas del ramio en el Valle del Cauca. *Acta Agronómica, Palmira, Colombia*. 17(3-4):17-7.

Calle Vélez, H., and A. Uribe. 1969. El cultivo del ramio para fibra y forrage. *Revista Cafetera de Colombia*. 18(145):39-50.

Coss, H. T., and J. L. Taylor.1948. Ramie today. *Textile Industry*. 112(8):99.

Ghosh, K., and T. Ghosh. 1971. Ramie cultivation in India. *Jute Bulletin*. Apr.-May. pp. 15-18.

Gómez Arias, N. 1968. El ramio en la producción de fibra de excelentes cualidades y fuerte de proteina para la alimentación animal. *Agriculture of the Tropics*. 14(11):787-90.

Kirby, R. H. 1963. *Vegetable Fibers, Botany, Cultivation, and Utilization*. Leonard Hill, London.

Naguib, A. M. 1967. Ramie–time of cultivating and development of growth during the life-time of the plant. *Agriculture Research Review U.A.R.* 43(3):77-97.

Rabechault, H. 1952. La ramie, études morphologiques et taxonomiques en vue de la sélection. *Revue Internationale des Produits Coloniaux*. 27:151-9.

Seale, C. C., E. O. Gangstad, and J. F. Joyner. 1953. *Agronomic Studies of Ramie in the Florida Everglades*. Florida Agriculture Experiment Station Bulletin 525. University of Florida, Gainesville, Florida, USA.

## Research Contacts and Germ Plasm Supply

Everglades Experiment Station, Belle Glade, Florida 33430, USA (H. V. Allison)

FAO Secretariat, Via delle Terme di Caracalla, 00100 Rome, Italy (D. Music and M. Petruszka)

# SPIRULINA

*Spirulina** species are blue-green algae often found in saline—usually alkaline—waters.† For many generations one species has been eaten in the Lake Chad area of Africa. In the 16th century the Spanish Conquistadores found the Aztecs using spirulina as their main source of protein. Some 60-70 percent of spirulina is good quality protein. It is also rich in vitamins and no harmful components have been found.

At Texcoco, near Mexico City, a new pilot plant has been set up to collect and process spirulina. About 1 ton of dry spirulina is produced daily; it is sold as a high-protein, high-carotene additive for chicken feed.

Extensive research has been conducted into the possibility of using spirulina as food for humans.

The algae's ability to thrive in highly saline and alkaline water is a great advantage. It grows well in waters containing up to 14,000 mg/liter of chloride, and of alkalinity up to pH 11. However, divalent ions, e.g., magnesium ions, must be properly balanced or eliminated. Seawater, for example, is not suitable because of its magnesium content. Carbon dioxide reacts chemically

*Spirulina platensis* (Chad species) [also known as *Arthrospira platensis*] and *Spirulina maxima* (Mexican species). Family: Cyanophyceae.

†For discussion of the importance to arid lands of vegetation that grows with saline water see *More Water for Arid Lands*. For information on ordering this companion report see page 187.

with the often alkaline culture medium, resulting in a high degree of carbon dioxide utilization. This makes growing of spirulina an efficient, productive process. Under favorable conditions production rates averaging $12 \text{ g/m}^2/\text{day}$ or more are possible.

Spirulina production involves culturing the alga in basins and then harvesting, washing, drying, and storing the product. Spirulina is large enough to be recovered from the culture medium by simple filtration. In Chad, villagers recover it by using muslin. This is spirulina's great advantage over other microorganisms that are often promoted as new protein sources, but are difficult and expensive to recover. Spray drying gives satisfactory results and does not damage spirulina's high nutritional properties. Heated roller drying also appears to give satisfactory results. Dried spirulina is not susceptible to fermentation and is easily stored. Solvents will bleach the green coloration to a pale, fawn color with almost no loss in nutritive value.

Spirulina can be added (up to 10 percent by volume) to cereals and other food products without changing the flavor or creating objectionable tastes. Spirulina's crude protein can reach as high as 72 percent (of dry matter) with a satisfactory balance of essential amino acids, except for a slight deficiency in the sulfur amino acids. It has a high vitamin content, particularly vitamin $B_{12}$. In rats the product was shown to have a digestibility of 84 percent with a net protein utilization of 61 and a protein efficiency ratio of 2.3 (casein was

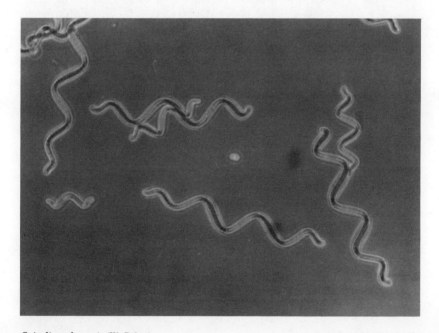

*Spirulina platensis* (W. Pabst)

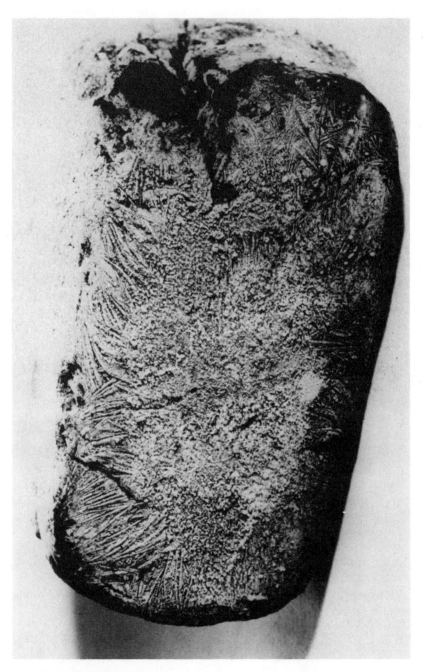

Frozen "loaf" of Spirulina. (FAO)

2.5). The nucleic acid content on a dry basis was 4.1 percent.* The tests showed no acute toxicity. Subchronic toxicity studies showed that dried alga (up to 10 percent) in the diet did not have any deleterious effects on the rats.

The cost of spirulina is heavily influenced by the production rate per unit area (which can be very high), the scale of manufacture, the life of the (polyethylene) covering over the production basins, the cost of decolorization, and the cost of land.

## LIMITATIONS AND SPECIAL REQUIREMENTS

Growing spirulina culture in artificial media requires a level of technical sophistication difficult to obtain in many developing nations.

Spirulina grows optimally at temperatures from 30°-35°C in arid or semiarid regions where there is little temperature variation.

Climates most favored for spirulina production are between latitudes 35° north and 35° south. Within this zone, the best locations are those with much sunlight, moderate rainfall, water of reasonable quality, and where there is a carbon dioxide source (such as natural gas or other hydrocarbons). Land should be inexpensive and reasonably flat.

If spirulina production is not carefully managed, bacteria or viruses can contaminate the product.

Data available at present are insufficient to predict the economics of spirulina production; more extensive feasibility studies are needed to justify investments.

## RESEARCH NEEDS

Further research and development is needed on mass cultivation of spirulina in artificial basins. Inexpensive watertight basins would greatly reduce investment costs. Improved $CO_2$ supplies and culture medium stirrers would also lower costs.

The highly promising laboratory results on mineral nutrition, salinity, carbon dioxide requirement, radiation, etc., need to be confirmed in field tests under actual operating conditions.

Harvesting and processing the algae are still relatively expensive and therefore require more research and development.

---

*This is a low nucleic acid: protein ratio compared to bacteria. For this reason spirulina can be eaten directly by humans without removal of the nucleic acids. Bacterial sources of protein cannot.

Spirulina is one alga that can be easily converted into a foodstuff. On the edge of Lake Chad, where it is native, a woman concentrates spirulina by pouring it into a cloth bag that allows the water to drain away . . .

... She then dries the residue in the sun and cuts it into the blocks which are cooked and eaten as a green vegetable. (Institute Français du Pétrole)

If mutants tolerant of magnesium ions can be found, spirulina could be grown in seawater. This would increase its utility and make it possible for it to grow in many more regions. Mutants with the ability to fix nitrogen would also be desirable.

Spirulina has been eaten for generations in Chad and Mexico. But before it can be considered absolutely safe for humans on a long-term basis, multigeneration feeding studies with animals and prolonged feeding tests with humans are required.

Social mores and eating habits have to be overcome before spirulina can become an acceptable human food additive.


## Selected Readings

Clement, G. 1970. An alga of high protein content. *Science, Progrès, Découverte.* 3423:39-46.

Clement, G. 1971. Une nouvelle algue alimentaire—la spiruline. *Revue De l'Institut Pasteur De Lyon.* 4(2):103-14.

Clement, G. and H. VanLandeghem. 1970. *Spirulina*: ein gunstiges Objekt fur die Massenkultur von Mikroalgen. *Berichte der Deutschen Botanischen Gesellschaft.* 83(11):559-65.

Hudson, B. J. F., and I. G. Karis. 1974. The lipids of the alga *Spirulina. Journal of the Science of Food and Agriculture.* 25:759-63.

Hiroshi, N. 1970. *The Mass Production of Spirulina—a Helical Blue-Green Algae as a New Food.* Microalgae International Union, Airlie Gardens, London.

Ogawa, T., and G. Terui. 1970. Studies on growth of *Spirulina platensis.* On the pure culture of *Spirulina platensis. Journal of Fermentation Technology.* 48(6):361-7.

Soeder, C. J., and W. Pabst. 1970. Aspects for the use of microalgae in feeding humans and animals. *Berichte der Deutschen Botanischen Gesellschaft.* 83(11):607-25.

The Protein Advisory Group of the United Nations. 1973. Proteins from microalgae and microfungi. *Tropical Science.* 15:77-81.

## Research Contacts and Germ Plasm Supply

Abteilung für Algen forschung der Gesellschaft für Strahlen and Umweltforschung, Bunsen-Kirchhoff-Strasse 13, D-46 Dortmund, Federal Republic of Germany (C. J. Soeder and H. D. Payer)

International Courses in Hydraulic and Sanitary Engineering, Oude Delft 95, Delft, Netherlands (J.W.M. la Riviere)

Institut Français du Petrole, Avenue de Bois-Préau, 92502 Rueil-Malmaison, France (G. Clement)

Limnology Lab, New University of Ulster, Traad Point, Drumenagh, Magherafelt, Co. Derry, Northern Ireland (B. Wood)

Research and Development Authority, Ben-Gurion University of the Negev, P.O. Box 1025, Beer-Sheva, Israel (A. Richmond)

Scripps Institute of Oceanography, University of California, La Jolla, California 92037, USA (R. Lewin)

# CONTRIBUTORS

SALEEM AHMED, Research Associate, The East-West Center, Honolulu, Hawaii, USA

R. V. ALLISON, Fiber Technologist Emeritus, University of Florida, Belle Glade, Florida, USA

W. P. BEMIS, Horticulturist, The University of Arizona, Tucson, Arizona, USA

BRENT BERLIN, Professor of Anthropology, University of California, Berkeley, California, USA

CAROLE S. BROW, University of California, Berkeley, California, USA

M. B. BURBAGE, Tropical Products Institute, London, England

H. M. BURKILL, Tropical Products Institute, Kew, England

GLENN W. BURTON, Research Geneticist, U.S. Department of Agriculture, Agriculture Research Service, Tifton, Georgia, USA

A. J. CANNING, Tropical Products Institute, London, England

GERONIMO CANO, Biology Department, Instituto Technologico y Estudios Superiores de Monterrey, Mexico

HARVEY T. CHAN, Jr., Research Food Technologist, U.S. Department of Agriculture, Agricultural Research Service, Hawaii Fruit Laboratory, Honolulu, Hawaii, USA

NELSON CHAVES, Instituto de Nutriçao da UFPe, Cidade Universitaria, Pernambuco, Brazil

J. A. CORNELIUS, Tropical Products Institute, London, England

D. G. COURSEY, Tropical Products Institute, London, England

ELSIE CROAL, Curator, Botanical Gardens, Georgetown, Guyana

J. M. DEMPSEY, Tropical Fiber Crops Specialist, University of Florida, Gainesville, Florida

R. DEVRED, Research Development Centre, FAO, Rome, Italy

M. G. C. McDONALD DOW, Deputy Director, BOSTID, NAS, Washington, D.C., USA

W. J. S. DOWNTON, Research Scientist, CSIRO, Merbein, Victoria, Australia

J. DRANSFIELD, Research Fellow, Royal Botanic Gardens, Kew, England

J. A. DUKE, Chief, Plant Taxonomy Laboratory, USDA/ARS, Beltsville, Maryland, USA

J. J. DUYVERMAN, Head, Advisory and Documentation Division, Royal Tropical Institute, Amsterdam, The Netherlands

M. A. M. EL-MAHDI, Director and Chairman of Botany, Wealth, Laboratory, Desert Institute, Mataria, Cairo, U.A.R.

L. T. EVANS, Chief of Division, CSIRO, Division of Plant Industry, Canberra City, Australia

R. FELGER, Arizona-Sonora Desert Museum, Tucson, Arizona, USA

A. GETAHUN, Associate Professor, College of Agriculture, Dire Dawa, Ethiopia

J. B. GILLETT, Botanist in Charge, East African Herbarium, Nairobi, Kenya

P. J. GREENWAY, Botanist, East African Agricultural Research Station, Amani, Tanga Region, Tanzania.

C. L. GREEN, Tropical Products Institute, London, England

A. GROBMAN, Director, Northrup, King & Co., Lima, Peru

A. SANTOS GUERRA, Ministerio de Agricultura, Departmento de Ecología y Botánica Aplicada, La Laguna, Tenerife

F HAGENZIEKER, Groningen, the Netherlands

J. J. HIGGINS, Research Plant Physiologist, USDA/ARS, Plant Introduction Station, Glenn Dale, Maryland, USA

W. H. HODGE, Senior Research Associate, L. H. Bailey Hortorium, Ithaca, New York, USA

G. E. INGLETT, Chief, Cereal Properties Laboratory, USDA/ARS, Peoria, Illinois, USA

H. S. IRWIN, President, The New York Botanical Garden, Bronx, New York, USA

D. B. JELLIFFE, M.D., Head, Division of Population, Family and International Health, University of California, Los Angeles, California, USA

B. JONES, Tropical Products Institute, London, England

Q. JONES, USDA/ARA, Beltsville, Maryland, USA

C. H. S. KABUYE, Botanist-in-Charge, East African Herbarium, Nairobi, Kenya

P. F. KNOWLES, Chairman and Professor, University of California, Davis, California, USA

E. LAING, Head, Department of Botany, University of Ghana, Legon, Ghana

S. P. LAU, Agriculture and Fisheries Department, Hong Kong Government, Hong Kong

J. LEON, Seed Production and Exchange Unit, Plant Production and Protection Division, FAO, Rome, Italy

T. R. N. LOTHIAN, Director, Botanic Garden, Adelaide, South Australia

G. C. LUGOD, Department of Botany, University of the Philippines, Laguna, Philippines

M. G. McGARRY, Visiting Research Fellow, University of Sussex, Brighton, England

C. M. McKELL, Director, Environment and Man Program, Utah State University, Logan, Utah, USA

C. P. McROY, Institute of Marine Science, University of Alaska, Fairbanks, Alaska, USA

R. McVAUGH, Director, University of Michigan Herbarium, Ann Arbor, Michigan, USA

J. R. MACONOCHIE, Senior Botanist, Arid Zone Research Institute, Alice Springs, Northern Territory, Australia

T. MAKEESO, Asst. Research Officer, Ethiopian Institute for Agricultural Research, Addis Ababa, Ethiopia

H. S. MANN, Director, Central Arid Zone Research Institute, Jodhpur, India

G. B. MASEFIELD, Department of Agricultural Science, University of Oxford, Oxford, England

F. G. MEYER, Research Botanist in Charge of the Herbarium, U.S. National Arboretum, Washington, D.C., USA

A. L. MYERS, Agricultural Engineer, USDA/ARS, Honolulu, Hawaii, USA

M. MADISON, Gray Herbarium, Cambridge, Massachusetts, USA

G. W. NEWELL, Director, Department of Toxicology, Stanford Research Institute, Menlo Park, California, USA

R. A. PERRY, Chief of Division, CSIRO, Land Resources Management, Wembley, Western Australia, Australia

G. B. PICKERING, Tropical Products Institute, London, England

R. W. POHL, Professor of Botany, Curator of the Herbarium, Iowa State University, Ames, Iowa, USA

H. POPENOE, International Programs in Agriculture, University of Florida, Gainesville, Florida, USA

J. V. POSSINGHAM, Chief of Division, CSIRO, Division of Horticultural Research, Adelaide, South Australia, Australia

J. W. PURSEGLOVE, East Malling Research Station, Kent, England

C. O. QUALSET, Professor, Department of Agronomy and Range Science, University of California, Davis, California, USA

P. RAVEN, Director, Missouri Botanical Garden, St. Louis, Missouri, USA

R. REITZ, Director, M.A.-I.B.D.F.-Jardim Botanico do Rio de Janeiro, Rio de Janeiro, Brazil

R. J. RODIN, Professor, Biological Sciences Department, California Polytechnic State University, San Luis Obispo, California, USA

R. ROLLINS, Gray Herbarium, Harvard University, Cambridge, Massachusetts, USA

R. ROSENGARTEN, Jr., Philadelphia, Pennsylvania, USA

P. ROSS, National Academy of Sciences, Washington, D.C., USA

J. RZEDOWSKI, Laboratorio de Botánica Fanerogámica, Instituto Politécnico Nacional, Mexico, DF, Mexico

P. E. SAJISE, Chairman, Department of Botany, University of the Philippines, Laguna, Philippines

H. SIOLI, Direktor am Max-Planck-Institut für Limnologie, Plön, Federal Republic of Germany

P. C. SPENSLEY, Tropical Products Institute, London, England

H. O'REILLY STERNBERG, Professor, Department of Geography, University of California, Berkeley, California, USA

B. C. STONE, Reader in Botany, Curator, University Herbarium, University of Malaya, Kuala Lumpur, Malaysia

D. SYMON, Head of Department, University of Adelaide, Adelaide, South Australia

K. TAKAMIYA, Regional Land and Water Development Officer, FAO, Santiago, Chile

D. E. TSURIEL, Chairman, International Cooperation on Sand Dune Reclamation, Haifa, Israel

N. VIVRETTE, Assistant Professor of Botany, University of California, Berkeley, California, USA

F. D. WILSON, Research Geneticist, USDA/ARS, Texas A & M University, College Station, Texas, USA

H. WILSON, Associate Instructor, Department of Plant Sciences, Indiana University, Bloomington, Indiana, USA

# RÉSUMÉ

Ce rapport traite de plantes tropicales choisies et prometteuses pour l'amélioration du régime alimentaire dans les zones tropicales. C'est là, en général, que l'on trouve les populations dont le revenu par tête est le plus bas du monde. En conséquence, il s'adresse à tous ceux qui aident les pays en voie de développement à parvenir à une exploitation plus rationnelle et plus équilibrée de leurs ressources. Ce sont aussi bien les gouvernements et le personnel d'assistance technique que les chercheurs qui s'occupent d'agriculture et de nutrition et de toutes les disciplines connexes.

En réponse à une enquête écrite, des scientifiques du monde entier ont mentionné quatre cents plantes. Parmi celles-ci, trente-six ont été retenues par un groupe ad hoc. Voici brièvement décrites, ces plantes prometteuses.

## Céréales et pseudocéréales

Millet cannelé (Channel millet) (*Echinochloa turnerana*)—Cette herbe sauvage d'Australie, qui n'a jamais encore été étudiée, peut produire des grains nutritifs avec un seul arrosage abondant. Ceci indique de grandes possibilités pour les terres arides où il ne pleut qu'à de rares intervalles.

Amaranthe à grains (espèce *Amaranthus*)—Cette céréale, presque complètement oubliée, d'Amérique centrale, produit des grains à forte teneur en protéines et en lysine, l'acide aminé nutritivement essentiel généralement absent dans les protéines végétales.

Quinoa (*Chenopodium quinoa*)—Bien que la graine de cette grande herbe présente l'une des meilleures sources de protéines de l'espèce végétale, le quinoa n'est pas cultivé en dehors de son habitat andin, en haute altitude.

Zostère (*Zostera marina*)—On pourrait entreprendre une recherche exploratoire fructueuse sur cette plante ressemblant à de l'herbe et produisant des graines. C'est une notion toute nouvelle et hautement spéculative que d'utiliser l'eau de mer pour les cultures céréalières. Toutefois, les Indiens de la côte occidentale du Mexique ont récolté de tout temps le grain de la zostère pour en faire de la farine et pour leur alimentation.

### Racines potagères et tubercules*

Pomme de terre celeri (*Arracacia xanthorrhiza*)–Cette plante, connue sous le nom de panais péruvien en raison du goût et de la texture de sa racine, ressemble au céleri. Elle est inconnue en dehors des régions andines d'altitude. Elle y est souvent cultivée à la place de la pomme de terre, son coût de production étant deux fois moins élevé. Les possibilités de la pomme de terre celeri n'ont pas encore été exploitées dans les terres d'altitude des tropiques du globe.

Yautia des anglo saxons (espèce *Xanthosoma*)–Ces plantes tubéreuses, hautement productives, ont un pouvoir nutritif plus élevé que la manioc et peuvent être cultivées facilement. Bien que leur aire de répartition soit très étendue, elles n'ont jamais fait l'objet d'essais appropriés permettant de définir leurs possibilités.

Talo et dasheens (*Colocasia esculenta*)–Le Talo, qui est cultivé sur une grande échelle dans un petit nombre seulement de pays, a un rendement élevé et offre de grandes possibilités pour toutes les régions tropicales. Certaines variétés poussent dans les hauteurs et d'autres dans des sols marécageux et saturés d'eau qui, autrement, seraient improductifs. Les dasheens, qui sont des variétés orientales, produisent de nombreux bulbes symétriques, de petite taille, à texture cassante et se conservant parfaitement.

### Légumes

Chaya (*cnidoscolus aconitifolius* et *cnidoscolus chayamansa*)–Les feuilles de ces plantes arbustives, prolifiques et à croissance rapide, fournissent un légume vert nutritif ressemblant à l'épinard. Connues seulement en Amérique centrale, elles mériteraient d'être essayées dans d'autres régions tropicales.

Coeurs de palmiers (*Euterpe, Guilielma, Acrocomis, Cocos,* etc.)–La faveur croissante dont jouit ce mets délicat rend inadéquats les approvisionnements actuels. Les peuplements sauvages se trouvent décimés, puisque l'enlèvement du bourgeon terminal tue le palmier. La culture en palmeraies semble très prometteuse et doit être encouragée avant l'extinction des peuplements sauvages.

Courage á la cire (*Benincasa hispida*)–Ce gros légume ressemble au melon. Il pousse facilement et peut donner trois récoltes annuelles. Sa caractéristique

---

*Igname (espèce *Dioscorea*)–Bien que l'igname soit trop connu pour figurer dans ce rapport, il représente l'une des cultures potagères tropicales les plus populaires et les plus nutritives. Toutefois, il n'est pas exploité autant que certains de ses concurrents parce que ses frais de production sont plus élevés. il serait donc très avantageux d'orienter la recherche vers la réduction de ces derniers et vers les problèmes du stockage. En effet, la plupart du temps, soixante pour cent des récoltes sont perdues à cause de la pourriture.

la plus intéressante est que le fruit peut être conservé, sans réfrigeration, pendant près d'un an.

Pois carré (*Psophocarpus tetragonolobus*)—Ce haricot grimpant, important en Asie du Sud-Est en Papoua-Nouvelle-Guinée, est inconnu ailleurs. Il pourrait être la contrepartie tropicale du soja. Soumis à une recherche appropriée, il pourrait éventuellement devenir la meilleure source de protéine utilisable dans les régions tropicales.

## Fruits

Durion (*espèce Durio*)—Le durion commun est un gros fruit épineux, très estimé par les uns, pour son goût et repoussé par les autres, à cause de son odeur. La récente découverte d'une espèce inodore pourrait s'avérer salutaire et satisfaire tout le monde. Un marché mondial pourrait alors s'ouvrir pour cette culture fruitière.

Mangoustan (*Garcinia mangostana*)—L'un, peut-être, des fruits les plus savoureux du monde, le mangoustan est peu connu en dehors de sa région natale, l'Asie du Sud-Est. Une recherche agronomique et horticole poussée permettrait de l'acclimater dans d'autres tropiques très humides. En effet, ce sont là des régions qui ne conviennent pas à la plupart des cultures.

Orange de Quito (*Solanum quitoense*)—Parent de la tomate, mais totalement différent, ce fruit est très estimé au Pérou, en Colombie, en Equateur et au Guatémala. Il est pratiquement inconnu ailleurs. Son jus délicieux et rafraîchissant pourrait être apprécié dans les zones tropicales d'Afrique et d'Asie où la plante pourrait prospérer facilement.

Pejibaye (*Guilielma gasipaes*)—Le fruit de ce palmier, ressemblant à une châtaigne, représente probablement l'aliment tropical le plus équilibré qui soit sur le plan nutritif. Il contient des hydrates de carbone, des protéines, de l'huile, des minéraux et des vitamines. Une fois établis, les arbres, qui conviennent aux tropiques humides, ne demandent que peu de soins tout en ayant un rendement très élevé.

Pamplemousse (*Citrus grandis*)—Ce gros fruit tropical, qui ne doit pas être confondu avec celui communément appelé par ce nom, est hautement apprécié dans tout le Sud-Est asiatique. Des cultivars de qualité supérieure pourraient présenter des possibilités, pour autant qu'on puisse les obtenir dans d'autres régions basses des tropiques. Dans les régions du monde où l'on cultive les agrumes, on a essayé des cultivars qui n'ont jamais atteint la qualité de ceux, les meilleurs, qui provenaient de la Thaïlande méridionale.

Corossel (*Annona muricata*)—Bien connue en Amérique tropicale la saveur riche et aromatique pourrait avoir une plus large audience. La pulpe et le jus de fruit se conservent bien et ce dernier pourrait ainsi faire l'objet d'exportations profitables vers les pays d'Europe et d'Amérique du Nord.

Uvilla (*Pourouma cecropiaefolia*)—Ce fruit, ressemblant à du raisin, est pratiquement inconnu en dehors de son aire de répartition dans la partie occidentale du bassin de l'Amazone. Sa chair est agréable quand il est mange cru. On peut également en faire du vin. Il mériterait d'être mis à l'essai dans d'autres régions forestières basses des tropiques. On ne sait absolument rien de sa biologie ni de ses possibilités culturales.

## Oléagineux

Babassú (*Orbignya speciosa*)—Ce palmier croît à profusion dans le bassin de l'Amazone et dans certaines régions de l'Amérique centrale. Bien que ses graines soient extrêmement riches en huile proche de celle du cocotier, le palmier babassú n'a jamais été cultivé. La main-d'oeuvre requise pour le ramassage des graines et la dureté de celles-ci, les rendant particulièrement difficiles à ouvrir, sont deux des obstacles à son exploitation.

Courge calebasse (*Cucurbita foetidissima*)—Elle pousse à l'état naturel dans les régions désertiques de l'Amérique du Nord et a depuis toujours fourni aux Indiens des grains comestibles. Ses mérites devraient être plus largement reconnus. Elle pourrait représenter, en effet, une source profitable d'huile alimentaire et des protéines dans les parties très arides du globe où il conviendrait d'établir des cultures d'essai.

Espèce *Caryocar*—Bien que le promoteur de l'industrie du caoutchouc, Sir Henry Wickham, ait encouragé cette source d'huile avec autant d'enthousiasme que l'hévéa, les arbres de l'espèce *Caryocar*, qui poussent à l'état sauvage en Amazonie, restent méconnus. Ils portent, en grande quantité, des noix oléagineuses ressemblant aux noix du Brésil.

*Jessenia polycarpa*—Originaire de l'Amazonie, ce palmier porte de très importants régimes de fruits dont l'huile est analogue en apparence, en teneur et en qualité à celle de l'olive. Elle est vendue comme huile alimentaire en Colombie mais est virtuellement inconnue dans le reste du monde.

Jojoba (*Simondsia cinensis*)—Cette plante des régions subtropicales de l'Amérique du Nord occupe une place unique dans le règne végétal. En effet, à l'inverse des autres végétaux, elle secrète une cire liquide dans ses graines, au lieu d'esters de glycérol. Les cires liquides sont importantes pour l'industrie. La seule autre source en est le cachalot. La mise sous culture du jojoba pourrait apporter ainsi de grands avantages économiques aux régions tropicales et subtropicales arides.

## Cultures fouragères

*Acacia albida*—C'est un arbre que l'on trouve dans les savanes de l'Afrique orientale et occidentale et dont le feuillage et les fruits, caractère insolite, apparaissent au cours de la saison sèche. Ses feuilles et ses gousses sont souvent le seul fourage disponible à cette époque. Toutes les espèces de bétail en sont très amateurs.

*Brosimum alicastrum*—Originaire d'Amérique centrale, c'est un grand arbre résistant à la sécheresse. Ses feuilles sont comestibles et ses fruits, petits, contiennent des graines amylacées. Le bétail est friand de son feuillage. Peu connu en dehors de son aire de dispersion, il mérite d'être essayé dans les régions tropicales—en particular celles qui ont des saisons sèches prolongées et où le fourage est indispensable.

Casse dense (*Cassia sturtii*)—Ce buisson est considéré sans importance dans son Australie natale. En Israël où il est cultivé expérimentalement, il fournit un fourage nutritif l'année durant. Il faudrait rechercher ses possibilités dans les autres régions arides des climats tempérés et subtropicaux.

Arroche (esp. *Atriplex*)—Plusieurs espèces de ces arbustes australiens semblent très prometteuses pour les régions arides. Elles produisent en abondance un fourage savoureux, particulièrement dans les sols salins.

Tamarugo (*Prosopis tamarugo*)—Cette légumineuse est un arbre rustique, natif du désert inhospitalier d'Atacama au Chili. Il pousse à travers une couche de sel pouvant atteindre un mètre. La qualité de ses gousses et de ses feuilles permet l'élevate du mouton à un rythme approchant celui des meilleures régions fouragères du monde.

### Divers

Palmier butiri (*Mauritia flexuosa*)—Bien qu'il soit le plus abondant du monde, ce palmier n'est pas exploité commercialement. Toutefois, dans son pays natal, le bassin de l'Amazone, on en tire à petite échelle des fruits, de l'amidon, des fibres et du bois. Il récompenserait largement les efforts de recherche et de développement qu'on lui consacrerait.

Candelilla (*Euphorbia antisyphilitica*)—Les feuilles de cette herbe provenant des régions désertiques du nord du Mexique sont recouvertes d'une cire de valeur. Elle est exploitée et expédiée aux Etats-Unis depuis plusieurs années par une industrie subventionnée par le gouvernement mexicain. La recherche orientée vers sa culture et son traitement pourrait en faire une récolte hautement profitable pour tous les sols arides des régions subtropicales.

Cauassú (*Calathea lutea*)—Cette grande herbe pousse à l'état sauvage dans les régions marécageuses du bassin de l'Amazone. Elle réussit tout aussi bien quand elle est cultivée en hauteur dans les zones à forte pluviosité. Ses feuilles sont recouvertes d'une cire dure qui fond facilement. Facile à planter et à récolter, le cauassú peut être exploité, dans les régions humides, dans des marais écartés qui seraient inutilisables autrement.

Guar (*Cyanopsis tetragonoloba*)—Les graines, à haute teneur en protéines, de cette plante asiatique qui ressemble au soja, renferment une gomme qui est de plus en plus recherchée par l'industrie. En raison de ses propriétés exceptionnelles, cette gomme a de nombreux usages qui vont de son emploi dans les tuyaux d'incendie, pour faire glisser l'eau plus facilement, jusqu'au durcissement de la crème glacée. De toutes les sources de gomme végétale, le guar est la plus prometteuse.

Guayule (*Parthenium argentatum*)—Arbuste des déserts du Mexique, il contient un latex comparable à celui de l'hévéa. Ce sont les problèmes techniques rencontrés dans la séparation du latex des résines et des autres matières végétales qui ont empéché son utilisation. Il recèle cependant de grandes promesses comme source de caoutchouc pour les régions arides.

Ramie (*Boehmeria nivea*)—La fibre extraite de ce grand arbuste d'Extrême-Orient est résistante et possède, entre autres qualités remarquables, celles de ne pas s'allonger et d'être irrétrécissable. Son exploitation est restreinte en raison de la gomme qui colle avec ténacité à la fibre. Dégommer cette dernière serait le premier problème à résoudre pour donner à la ramie la place qui pourrait lui revenir dans l'agriculture tropicale.

*Paspalum vaginatum*—Cette herbe extrêmement tolérante au sel supporte parfaitement les innondations d'eau salée. Elle est recommandée pour reconstituer la végétation des régions envahies par le sel. Elle est particulièrement appropriée pour fixer le sable des plages. Déjà cultivée avec succès en Australie, elle fournit du fourage dans les marais côtiers qui, par ailleurs, seraient improductifs.

Spirulina (*Spirulina platensis* et *Spirulina maxima*)—Ces algues à haute teneur en protéines poussent dans les eaux saumâtres et alcalines. A l'inverse de certaines autres algues, les grand rassemblements de spirulina permettent de la récolter facilement avec des filets ou d'autres moyens aussi simples. Elle est agréable au goût et, au Tchad et au Mexique, elle fait déjà partie du régime alimentaire.

# RESUMEN

Este es un informe sobre plantas tropicales escogidas que tienen la posibilidad de mejorar la calidad de vida en las zonas tropicales. En términos generales los países de esta zona contienen las poblaciones de más bajos ingresos en todo el mundo. De ahí que este informe se dirija a aquellos que se preocupan por ayudar a los países en desarrollo a obtener un aprovechamiento más eficiente y balanceado de sus recursos biológicos: administradores gubernamentales, personal técnico asistente, investigadores agrícolas, en nutrición y disciplinas afines.

Las 36 plantas que aquí se describen fueron escogidas por un grupo de entre 400 personas que habían sido nombradas por expertos en plantas de todo el mundo en respuesta a una indagación por escrito.

A continuación se da un resumen de las plantas escogidas por las grandes posibilidades que ofrecen.

### Cereales y pseudócereales

Mijo de canal (*Echinochloa turnerana*). Este pasto silvestre de Australia, que jamás se ha estudiado, da un grano nutritivo con sólo regarlo profundamente una vez, lo cual indica el potencial para aquellas tierras áridas donde llueve escasamente.

Grano amaranto (*Amaranthus* spp.). Las semillas de este casi totalmente descuidado grano contienen un nivel sumamente alto de proteínas y del aminoácido nutritivo esencial—la licina—que por lo general no se halla con regularidad en las proteínas de las plantas.

Quinua (*Chenopodium quinoa*). A pesar de que la semilla de esta alta espiga es una de las mejores fuentes de proteína en el reino vegetal, la quinua no se cultiva fuera de su ambiente andino de grandes alturas.

*Zostera marina*. Los estudios de exploración sobre esta planta podrán resultar en copiosos beneficios por cuanto es una planta parecida a la hierba que crece en el agua salada y que produce grano. El uso del mar para cultivar grano es un concepto nuevo y de mucha especulación, pero los indios de la costa occidental de México por tradición han cultivado el grano de la Zostera marina para alimento y harina.

### Raíces y tubérculos*

Arracacha (*Arracacia xanthorrhiza*). Es conocida como pastinaca peruana debido al sabor y a la textura de su raíz. Esta planta, que se asemeja al apio, es desconocida fuera del altiplano andino. En esta región con frecuencia se cultiva esta raíz en lugar de la papa. Su costo de producción es sólo la mitad. La arracacha cuenta con un potencial aún no explotado en las altas regiones tropicales del mundo.

Yautia (*Xanthosoma* spp.). Estas raíces altamente productivas son más nutritivas que la mandioca (cazabe) y muy faciles de cultivar. A pesar de encontrarse ampliamente distribuídas, no se las ha estudiado con detenimiento para saber cuáles son sus posibilidades.

Taro y Dasheens (*Colocasia esculenta*). Sólo en muy pocos países se cultivan en gran escala, pero el taro, que es altamente productivo, tiene muy buenas posibilidades de cultivo en las regiones tropicales del mundo. Algunos tipos crecen en tierra alta, otros en suelos anegados y cenagosos que no producirían otros alimentos. Dasheens son variedades orientales que producen un sin número de bulbos pequeños y simétricos de textura vigorosa y que pueden almacenarse sin peligro que se dañen.

### Vegetales

Chaya (*Cnidoscolus aconitifolius* y *Cnidoscolus chayamansa*). Estos arbustos de crecimiento y proliferación rápidos proveen un vegetal verde nutritivo y parecido a la espinaca. Aunque se la conoce sólo en Centroamérica, merece que se la pruebe en otras regiones tropicales.

Palmito (*Euterpe, Guilielma, Acrocomis, Cocos*, etc.). Durante los últimos diez años la demanda de este manjar ha crecido tanto que los abastecimientos actuales son inadecuados. Las palmas silvestres se están diezmando puesto que al extraerles el corazón se las mata. Se debe promover el cultivo de la palma porque ofrece muy buenas posibilidades antes de que las silvestres sean destruídas.

Calabaza amarilla (*Benincasa hispida*). Este vegetal grande parecido al melón es fácil de cultivar y puede producir tres cosechas al año. La

---

*Batatas (*Dioscorea* spp.). Aunque las batatas son muy bien conocidas para que se las incluya en este informe, estas son las más nutritivas y populares de las cosechas de raíces tropicales. Sin embargo, no se cultivan con tanta amplitud como algunas de sus competidoras porque su costo de producción es más alto; la inversión en el studio para reducir su costo de producción sería de extremo valor. Asimismo es necesario estudiar los problemas de almacenamiento: alrededor del 60% de las cosechas muy a menudo se pierde o se pudre.

característica sobresaliente es que la fruta puede guardarse hasta por doce meses sin refrigeración.

Frijol alado *(Psophocarpus tetragonolobus)*. Este frijol trepador, de importancia en el sudeste de Asia y Papua Nueva Guinea, pero desconocido en otras partes, posiblemente sea la contrapartida del frijol de soya. Con algunos estudios, posiblemente llegaría a ser una de las mejores fuentes de proteína útil en los trópicos.

## Frutas

Durian *(Durio* spp.). El durian común es una fruta grande, espinosa y estimada por muchos por su sabor, pero aborrecida por otros por su olor. El descubrimiento de una especie que no tenga ese olor ofensivo podría ser más aceptable y abriría un mercado mundial a este producto.

Mangostán *(Garcinia mangostana)*. El mangostán, tal vez una de las frutas de mejor sabor en el mundo, es muy poco conocida fuera del sudeste de Asia. Las investigaciones agronómicas y en la horticultura a fondo contribuirían a extender su área de cultivo a otras regiones sumamente húmedas del trópico—una zona cuyo clima no se presta para el cultivo de la mayoría de las siembras.

Naranjilla *(Solanum quitoense)*. Esta fruta usada como postre, aunque es de la familia del tomate pero no se parece a éste, es muy apetecida en Perú, Colombia, Ecuador y Guatemala y, sin embargo, es virtualmente desconocida en otras partes. Su jugo es delicioso y refrescante y podría ser popular en la zona tropical de Africa y Asia, donde la planta podría florecer con facilidad.

Pejibaye *(Guilielma gasipaes)*. La fruta de esta palma, parecida a la castaña, es probablemente el alimento tropical nutritivo mejor balanceado. Contiene carbohidratos, proteína, aceite, minerales y vitaminas. Propias del trópico húmedo, las palmeras, una vez establecidas, requieren muy poco cuidado y dan una abundante cosecha.

Pomelo *(Citrus grandis)*. Esta fruta de tamaño grande, posiblemente de la familia de la toronja, es de gran estima en todo el sudeste de Asia. El cultivo de variedades distintas podría ofrecer excelentes posibilidades si éstas pudieran darse en tierras bajas tropicales. Si bien ésta se ha probado ampliamente en las regiones cítricas del mundo, la calidad de las variedades probadas nunca se asemeja a las mejores del sur de Tailandia.

Guanábana *(Annona muricata)*. Esta fruta es bien conocida en la región tropical de América y tiene un sabor rico y aromático que podría disfrutarse más ampliamente. Tanto el jugo como la pulpa se conservan bien y su eportación de países tropicales a Europa y Norteamérica podría ofrecer buenas posibilidades económicas.

Uvilla *(Pourouma cecropiaefolia)*. Esta fruta parecida a la uva es casi desconocida fuera de su tierra natal al occidente de la cuenca del Amazonas. Su pulpa, que es de sabor agradable, se come cruda y también sirve para hacer vino. Esta merece que se la pruebe en otras regiones bajas montañosas del trópico. No se sabe absolutamente nada en cuanto a sus posibilidades biológicas o agronómicas.

## Semillas oleaginosas

Babassú (*Orbignya speciosa*). Esta palma crece abundantemente en la cuenca del Amazonas y algunos lugares de Centroamérica. Aunque las semillas son ricas en aceite, muy parecido al aceite de coco, la palma babassú no ha sido aún cultivada. Las barreras principales que se interponen a su explotación son el trabajo necesario para recolectar las semillas y el hecho que éstas son extremadamente duras y no se abren con facilidad.

Calabaza búfalo (*Curcurbita foetidissima*). Esta calabaza silvestre del desierto norteamericano, la cual provee de semillas comestibles a los indios de Norteamérica, es una posible fuente provechosa de aceite comestible y proteína en tierras extremadamente áridas. Merece que se la reconozca con más amplitud y se la cultive en forma experimental en todas las regiones áridas del mundo.

Especies de *Caryocar*. A pesar de que Sir Henry Wickham, el pionero en la industria del caucho en Malaya, promovió esta fuente de aceite con el mismo entusiasmo con que promovió el árbol de caucho, la especie *Caryocar* continúa creciendo en forma silvestre en la región del Amazonas sin que se le preste mucha atención. Estos árboles producen grandes cantidades de semillas oleaginosas parecidas a la nuez del Brasil.

*Jessenia polycarpa*. Esta palma, oriunda de la región amazónica, produce unos racimos extraordinariamente grandes de una fruta que tiene un aceite parecido al de la aceituna en apariencia, contenido y calidad. Se vende como aceite comestible en Bogotá, Colombia, pero es casi desconocida en el resto del mundo.

Jojoba (*Simmondsia chinensis*). Esta planta subtropical de Norteamérica es especial en el reino vegetal: segrega cera líquida en sus semillas en vez de los aceites glicéridos que otras plantas segregan. En la industria, las ceras líquidas son de importancia. Estas son difíciles de sintetizar y la única otra fuente es el cachalote. El desarrollo de la jojoba como producto de cultivo promete importantes beneficios económicos a las regiones áridas tropicales y subtropicales.

## Forrajes

*Acacia albida*. Este árbol leguminoso que crece en las sabanas del Africa Oriental y Occidental, es poco común por el hecho de producir follaje y fruto durante la estación seca. Sus hojas y vainas, con frecuencia, constituyen el único forraje disponible en esa época y, por lo tanto, muy apetecido por toda clase de ganado.

*Brosimum alicastrum*. Este árbol alto y resistente a la sequía es propio de Centroamérica. Produce hojas nutritivas y una fruta pequeña con semillas feculentas. Sus hojas son favoritas del ganado. Poco se sabe acerca de este árbol fuera de Centroamérica y merece que se lo pruebe en zonas tropicales—especialmente en aquellas donde la estación seca es prolongada— donde se necesita una fuente de forraje.

Dense Cassia (*Cassia sturtii*). Esta mata de poca importancia como forraje en Australia, su tierra nativa, está dando un forraje nutritivo todo el año en proyectos de experimentación que se llevan a cabo en Israel. Se determinará su necesidad potencial en otras regiones áridas de clima templado o subtropical.

Matas salinas (*Atriplex* spp.). Varias especies australianas de estos arbustos ofrecen grandes posibilidades para las regiones áridas. Estas producen un abundante forraje de buen gusto, especialmente en suelos salinos.

Tamarugo (*Prosopis tamarugo*). Este árbol leguminoso, duro, nativo del aborrecible Desierto de Atacama, en Chile, crece a través de una capa de sal a veces de un metro de espesor. La calidad de sus cápsulas y hojas permite que se alimenten ovejas casi en la misma proporción en que se hace en las mejores zonas forrajeras del mundo.

## Misceláneas

Palma Burití (*Mauritia flexuosa*). Posiblemente ésta sea la palmera más abundante en todo el mundo, pero no tiene ningún uso comercial. Sin embargo, un buen número de productos—almidón, fruta, fibra y madera—se obtienen de ella en pequeña escala en la cuenca del Amazonas, su lugar nativo. Esta es una fuente abundante que muy bien compensará su investigación y desarrollo.

Candelilla (*Euphorbia anitsyphilitica*). Esta hierba de los desiertos del norte de México tiene unas hojas cubiertas de una cera valiosa. Una empresa mexicana con subsidio la ha producido y exportado a los Estados Unidos durante varios años. El estudio, elaboración y cultivo de la candelilla puede convertirla en un producto altamente provechoso en las tierras áridas en toda la región subtropical.

Cauassú (*Calathea lutea*). Esta hierba silvestre crece alta en ciénagas de la cuenca del Amazonas, pero también crece bien en plantaciones en las laderas de cerros en regiones de lluvias abundantes. Sus hojas están cubiertas de una cera dura y de alta fusión. La cauassú, que es sencilla de sembrar y cultivar, puede producirse en ciénagas remotas inservibles de zonas húmedas.

Guar (*Cyanopsis tetragonoloba*). Las semillas de alto contenido protínico de esta planta asiática, que se asemeja a la planta del frijol de soya, contienen una goma de demanda creciente en la industria. Debido a sus propiedades especiales, la goma tiene varios usos, desde permitir que el agua fluya con más facilidad a través de una manguera de incendio hasta endurecer helados. El guar es la fuente de goma más prometedora entre los vegetales.

Guayule (*Parthenium argentatum*). Este es un arbusto de los desiertos mexicanos que contiene buena cantidad de latex que se asemeja mucho al hule *Hevea*. Su desarrollo ha sido impedido por problemas técnicos asociados con la separación del latex de las resinas y otra materia vegetal. Sin embargo, como fuente de caucho en regiones áridas, el guayule ofrece grandes posibilidades.

Ramio (*Boehmeria nivea*). La fibra de este arbusto alto y perenne proveniente del Asia Oriental posee cualidades superiores—fuerte y no se estira ni se encoge como otras. Sin embargo, su desarrollo es restringido porque posee una goma que se adhiere fuertemente a la fibra. Cuando se solucione el problema de extraerle la goma, esto constituirá el primer paso para darle al ramio un papel de mayor significado en la agricultura tropical.

Hierba de aluvión (*Paspalum vaginatum*). Esta hierba altamente tolerante a la sal resiste inundaciones de agua de mar y se recomienda para la producción de nueva vegetación de regiones afectadas por la sal. En especial, es buena para dar estabilidad a las playas arenosas. Esta herba, que ya se ha cultivado con éxito en Australia, provee forraje en ciénagas costeras que de lo contrario no se usarían.

Espirulina (*Spirulina platensis* y *Spirulina maxima*). Estas algas de alto contenido proteínico crecen en aguas saladas y alcalinas. Contrario a otras algas, los grandes conjuntos de espirulina permiten su cosecha con red o cualquier otro método sencillo. Es agradable al paladar y ya se usa para consumo humano en Chad y en México.

185

BOARD ON SCIENCE AND TECHNOLOGY FOR
INTERNATIONAL DEVELOPMENT
COMMISSION ON INTERNATIONAL RELATIONS
NATIONAL ACADEMY OF SCIENCES—NATIONAL RESEARCH COUNCIL
2101 Constitution Avenue, Washnigton, D.C. 20418, USA

## ADVISORY STUDIES AND SPECIAL REPORTS

### PUBLISHED

1. **East Pakistan Land and Water Development as Related to Agriculture.** January 1971. 67 p. (out of print) Reviews World Bank proposed action program in land and water management. NTIS Accession No. PB 203-328. $4.25.
2. **The International Development Institute.** July 1971. 57 p. Endorses concepts of new science-based technical assistance agency as successor to AID; examines its character, purposes, and functions.
3. **Solar Energy in Developing Countries: Perspectives and Prospects.** March 1972. 49 p. (out of print) Assesses state of art, identifies promising areas for R & D, and proposes multipurpose regional energy research institute for developing world. NTIS Accession No. PB 208-550. $4.25.
4. **Scientific and Technical Information for Developing Countries.** April 1972. 80 p. (out of print) Examines problem of developing world's access to scientific and technical information sources, provides rationale for assistance in this field, and suggests programs for strengthening information infrastructure and promoting information transfer. NTIS Accession No. PB 210-107. $4.75.
6. **Research Management and Technical Entrepreneurship: A U.S. Role in Improving Skills in Developing Countries.** 1973. 40 p. Recommends initiation of a systematic program and indicates priority elements.
7. **U.S. International Firms and R, D & E in Developing Countries.** 1973. 92 p. Discusses aims and interests of international firms and developing-country hosts and suggests that differences could be mitigated by sustained efforts by the firms to strengthen local R, D & E capabilities.
8. **Ferrocement: Applications in Developing Countries.** 1973. 89 p. Assesses state of the art and cites applications of particular interest to developing countries—boatbuilding, construction, food- and water-storage facilities, etc.
9. **Mosquito Control: Some Perspectives for Developing Countries.** 1973. 63 p. Examines biological-control alternatives to conventional pesticides; evaluates state of knowledge and research potential of several approaches.
10. **Food Science in Developing Countries: A Selection of Unsolved Problems.** 1974. 81 p. Describes 42 unsolved technical problems with background information, possible approaches to a solution, and information sources.
11. **Aquatic Weed Management: Some Perspectives for Guyana.** 1973. 44 p. Report of workshop with the National Science Research Council of Guyana describes new methods of aquatic weed control suitable for tropical developing countries.

187

12. **Roofing in Developing Countries: Research for New Technologies.** 1974. 74 p. (out of print) Emphasizes the need for research on low cost roofs, particularly using materials available in developing countries. NTIS Accession No. PB 234-503/AS. $4.75.
13. **Meeting the Challenge of Industrialization: A Feasibility Study for an International Industrialization Institute.** 1973. 133 p. Advances concept of an independent, interdisciplinary research institute to illuminate new policy options confronting all nations.
14. **More Water for Arid Lands: Promising Technologies and Research Opportunities.** 1974. 153 p. Outlines little-known but promising technologies to supply and conserve water in arid areas.
15. **International Development Programs of the Office of the Foreign Secretary**, by Harrison Brown and Theresa Tellez. 1973. 68 p. History and analysis, 1963-1972; lists staff/participants and publications.
16. **Underexploited Tropical Plants with Promising Economic Value.** 1975.
17. **The Winged Bean: A High Protein Crop for the Tropics.** 1975. 43 p. Describes a neglected tropical legume from Southeast Asia and Papua-New Guinea that appears to have promise for combatting malnutrition in tropical areas around the world.

## IN PREPARATION (Working Titles)

5. The Role of U.S. Engineering Schools in Foreign Assistance Activities.
18. Energy for Rural Development: Renewable Resources and Alternative Technologies for Developing Countries.
19. Methane Generation from Human, Animal and Agricultural Wastes.
20. Systems Analysis and Operations Research: A Tool for Policy and Program Planning for Developing Countries
21. The Productive Utilization of Freshwater Aquatic Weeds: Research Opportunities for Developing Countries.
22. Guayule: Rubber Producing Desert Shrub.

**Related Publications:** Other reports (which BOSTID helped prepare) available from the above address are: **An International Centre for Manatee Research.** 1975. 34 p. Describes the use of the manatee, a large, almost extinct, marine mammal, to clear aquatic weeds from canals. Proposes a research laboratory to develop manatee reproduction and husbandry. Published by the National Science Research Council of Guyana.
**Products from Jojoba; a Promising New Crop for Arid Lands.** 1975. 30 p. Describes the chemistry of the oil obtained from the North American desert shrub *Simmondsia chinensis.*

### How to Order

**Published reports (unless out of print)** are available free on request from the Board on Science and Technology for International Development. BOSTID will fill requests for reports in preparation upon publication. **Out-of-print reports** are available from the National Technical Information Service. To order, send report title, NTIS Accession Number, and amount indicated. Pay by NTIS Deposit Account, check or money order. U.S. orders without prepayment are billed within 15 days; a 50¢ charge is added. Foreign buyers must enclose payment plus U.S. $2.50 handling charge per item. Send order to

National Technical Information Service
Springfield, Virginia 22161, USA

**ORDER FORM**

*Please indicate on the labels below the names of colleagues, institutions, libraries, etc., that might be interested in receiving a copy of* Underexploited Tropical Plants with Promising Economic Value.

*Please return this form to*

> Commission on International Relations (JH 215)
> National Academy of Sciences-National Research Council
> 2101 Constitution Avenue
> Washington, D.C. 20418, USA

16

16

16

16

16

16